This book belongs to

Fred Dibnah

The Fred Dibnah Legacy

Introduction

Was it that the man could hypnotise us with his deep and unique Bolton accent? Or the fact that during a demolition he could stand only 10ft away from a 200ft brick chimney as it thundered towards earth for the last time. Could it be that we were dazzled by his head for heights, as he dangled from the top of a very tall Victorian chimney on a Bosons chair, humming as he swung 180ft from tera-firma? Or are we a nation of steam lovers, and Fred Dibnah unlocked our interest and desire for knowledge of these relics from the past?

Fred Dibnah some how managed to turn us into a nation of voyeurs. Six million viewers would tune into BBC2 at 8pm every week to watch the next episode of his series, 'A year with Fred' – we were hooked on what he had been up to. He might knock down a chimney brick by brick, throwing his Embassy cigarette butt down with the bricks as he took in the view from high above. He might be driving his steam roller down the cobbled stone back streets of Bolton. We might watch him demolish a massive chimney that he had propped up on telegraph poles, before setting light to them. Maybe it was the way he talked about life, and how he would put the world to rights. Or Fred taking his family to Blackpool for a holiday, but then sneaking off and using his wife as a labourer as he knocked down a small factory chimney one brick at a time so that he could get a part made for his steam roller.

Perhaps there is a simple answer. Perhaps Fred Dibnah was the ultimate Working Class Hero. We had never seen the like of someone like him before on our television sets. You can only imagine what film producer Don Haworth thought when meeting Fred for the first time? Word has it that Don had watched a news item about Fred in an edit suite back at BBC Manchester, and was so entranced by what he saw, that the next day went to Bolton Town Hall to meet and observe the Bolton Steeplejack. I am sure that Don very quickly realised that he had discovered television gold dust within the first five minutes of meeting Fred Dibnah. Don had made a good number of documentaries for

Compiled and researched by Paul Donoghue
Art Editor: Rob Callaghan
All photographs and documents are taken from The Paul Donoghue Heritage collection.
Design/Illustrations: Trevor Hamlett, Brian Smith
Reformatting of the original Fred Dibnah Steams On book by kind permission of Peter Nicholson.
Website: www.freddibnah.tv

Digital Production Manager: Nicky Baker

Management
Bookazine Manager: Dharmesh Mistry
Production Director: Robin Ryan
Managing Director of Advertising: Julian Lloyd-Evans
Newstrade Director: Martin Belson
Chief Operating Officer: Brett Reynolds
Group Finance Director: Ian Leggett
Chief Executive: James Tye
Chairman: Felix Dennis

MagBook
The MagBook brand is a trademark of Dennis Publishing Ltd, 30 Cleveland St, London W1T 4JD. Company registered in England. All material © Paul Donoghue & Dennis Publishing Ltd, licensed by Felden 2010, and may not be reproduced in whole or part without the consent of the publishers. Fred Dibnah's World of Steam, ISBN 978-1-907232-46-6.

Licensing
To license this product, please contact Winnie Liesenfeld on +44 (0) 20 7907 6134 or email winnie_liesenfeld@dennis.co.uk

Liability
While every care was taken during the production of this MagBook, the publishers cannot be held responsible for the accuracy of the information or any consequence arising from it. Dennis Publishing takes no responsibility for the companies advertising in this MagBook.

The paper used within this MagBook is produced from sustainable fibre, manufactured by mills with a valid chain of custody. Printed at BGP.

MAGBOOK

Dr Frederick Dibnah MBE 1938 - 2004

the BBC in the past, he had a track record, and he knew his game. The man before him was completely different from anyone he had ever met before. From day one he noticed that Fred Dibnah had no fear of the cameras, and Fred had that rare gift of being exactly the same person whether a camera crew was there or not. I know from my own experience of filming Fred that you only had to prompt him with a question, and off he would go, arms out, scratching his chin, moving his flat cap here and there across his bald head. The end result was that Fred always made the piece interesting for whoever might be watching and listening to the finished product or programme. Don managed to bag Fred, and a BBC contract was quickly signed. Don's first documentary, 'Fred Dibnah Steeplejack' won him a coveted BAFTA award. Like I say, television gold dust.

They say that from little acorns, oak trees grow. Well, that was certainly the case with Fred Dibnah. As a young man I used to watch Fred's documentaries on the TV. I was a young strapping lad into The Bay City Rollers and Gary Glitter (please forgive me). But, I still found time for Fred. I was one of the many millions who were under Fred's spell. You could see Fred's fame growing year by year. Vodaphone and beer adverts, Redland Bricks and then low and behold he was on Russell Harty's chat show. I'll never forget that interview. Fred sits down and once settled asks Russell, 'Do you mind if I smoke?' Every time you picked up a paper it was Fred Dibnah this, or Fred Dibnah that. Quiet funny really until Alison and the kids left him. At this traumatic stage in someone's life you would expect them to tell the cameras, soundman, producer and the rest of the entourage to bugger off, and shout I'm having a bad day, leave me alone. Not Fred. He told the whole wide world what had happened to him. It was like the ultimate soap opera. And the plot was fantastic, you couldn't write it if you tried.

I worked in a factory back then as a machine tool painter, it was a proper bloke's environment. During the dinner hour we all sat in a circle in the workshop drinking tea, and opening our Tupperware boxes to see what delights we had to eat. Looking back it was mad; there was this ritual you see. Someone would start to eat a sandwich,

and someone else would ask what you had. "Sandwich spread mate," and then it went round the circle as everyone revealed what they had in their box. Ham and egg, spam and brown sauce, chicken salad etc. When it came to me the answer was always the same. Cheese and Branston Pickle. I can't ever forget it, for that's what my Mum packed me for lunch every working day for two years. Then someone would pipe up. "What about poor old Fred Dibnah eh?" And off we went. The debate was called to order. You see Fred was a hero to all working men. A God, he smoked fags, drank beer, and when he spoke we listened. He was always bang on, what Fred said was true, and it struck a chord with us factory men. The country had indeed gone to the dogs, he said. Fred told us what he would do with vandals after they had smashed up the headstones in a graveyard. He moaned that Great Britain was no longer the workshop to the world. It was a fact that we didn't make anything anymore, and yes, when he said "We've become a nation of con men, living by selling double-glazing to each other, and the modern world stinks," the men in my workplace gave a very loud "Here! Here!" Someone would then continue the Dibnah debate. "See his wife Alison and the kids have left him?"

Fred Dibnah wore his heart on his sleeve, you see. We all watched as he poured his heart out on national telly and told the nation that they wanted a divorce. Alison had gone to Greece for a holiday, came back and promptly packed her things and left Fred. She must have had enough of the Victorian lifestyle offered by Fred and voted with her feet. Poor Fred took it all very personally and you could see that the poor fellow was heartbroken. What we were watching was reality TV, long before the phrase had even been invented.

While all this was being filmed, and with Fred close to tears at times, I can imagine Don thinking to himself, 'here comes another BAFTA'.

So the credits roll and James Gallway plays his flute to Fred's theme tune, 'The carnival of Venice'. I carry on listening to the Bay City Rollers. I've gone off Gary Glitter a bit, and I'm now into Mud, Suzy Quatro and Alvin Stardust. The series has ended so Fred Dibnah's off the

Fred Dibnah ready to go underground as he visits a coal mine.

Fred almost at the top a mill chimney as he negotiates climbing over the lip.

telly for a while. I thought that was it. That Fred Dibnah had been and gone. There was nowt in the papers. It was all very quiet on the Dibnah front. Then my Grandad bought me a copy of the book Fred Dibnah Steeplejack for Christmas, so I think I must have been a fan. Then before you know it Fred's back on TV. He's got a new lady that doesn't like him smoking. He's still knocking down chimneys. The second traction engine is still in bits in the shed, and he's back in the newspapers. What we didn't know back then was that Fred Dibnah would be popping in and out of our lives for the next few decades.

As the custodian of Fred Dibnah's photograph and document archive I can assure you that I know my subject well. People like Fred Dibnah are a very rare commodity. From a very young age, Fred wanted to be the best steeplejack in the whole country. It was his life. This bloke drew pictures of steeplejacks as he looked out of his classroom window. His hero was John Faulkner the Manchester Steeplejack. As a teenager he scrambled up Bolton's tallest chimney and did a mock hanging with a tailor's dummy. From the ground looking up it appeared as though someone had committed suicide. He had done it for a ten bob bet. I particularly like the fact that while he was up there he erected two union jack flags.

Everyone in Bolton knew who Fred Dibnah was, and now five years after his passing the whole country still remembers the flat capped man from Bolton 'Fred Dibnah Steeplejack'.

This new MagBook carries on the story from where we left off with our first effort, 'Fred Dibnah, The Early Days'. Once again, I have delved into the Dibnah archive and set about recreating (and updating) one of Fred's early books. With the assistance of modern technology (not sure if Fred would approve) and some fabulous documents and photographs, I have managed to bring back to life one of Fred Dibnah's greatest works. Enjoy!

Paul Donoghue

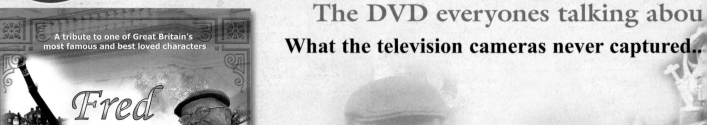

Contents

Alison The Steam Roller   *pg 10*

Starting All Over Again   *pg 30*

Stationary Steam   *pg 44*

More Chimney Pieces   *pg 58*

The German Connection   *pg 74*

The Famous Fred   *pg 82*

The Rise and Fall of King Steam   *pg 98*

Scrapbook   *pg 112*

A proud looking Fred Dibnah with his much loved
Aveling & Porter steam roller.

Chapter one

Alison
The Steam Roller

In 1966 I bought a steam roller that were absolutely knackered. The rear wheels sloped inwards and the water tank at the back was full of holes, all the bearings were shot out of it and you could see daylight through the funnel and the smokebox.

This was Aveling & Porter No. 7632 built in February 1912, and represented something I had longed to own for many years and so despite its condition, I had jumped at the chance to buy it. I bought this specimen off two Welsh scrap iron merchants for £175, not that I ever got a receipt for it. They dragged it out of a shed and onto a country lane and just left it there, beside the road. All 12 tons of it, most of which appeared to be rust. I gave them the money and off they went leaving me to it. Fortunately for me I knew this farmer who had an 1899 Foden traction engine and he agreed to tow it from the old army camp where we had found it, to his farm which was a distance of about seven miles. We eventually got there, not having had too much experience with steam engines. I had steered one or two of them before and that were about it really. We then played about with it for

a couple of weeks until this chap, a sort of an engineer who used to come and fettle up the farmer's engine from time to time, came along and gave it a look over.

He told us what he thought were wrong with it. He told us to change this and do that before we should attempt the journey home to Bolton, which were a distance of about nine miles. We did what he said and then on the next Sunday morning we arrived at the farm at about 7.00 am and lit the fire. The engineer chap agreed to drive the engine, it being the first time it had travelled under its own steam for nearly 20 years. This was a big moment as we proudly set off, bound for Bolton.

We got about four miles down the road and the thing conked out on us. However, in a matter of three or four weeks we had learnt quite a bit about steam rollers and realised that the trouble was with the injector, the thing that puts the water into the boiler. This were completely blocked up with muck so we removed it and took it home and had a good look at it. We then took it round to the local brass foundry for some expert attention. The fellow there had a quick look at it and said,

"I don't want to take your money off you cock. So take it home, throw it in the fire, then take it outside and bang it on the flags. These brass cones will fall out and all the muck'll fall out."

Fred Dibnah's newly purchased Aveling & Porter 12-ton steam roller No. 7632 parked on Silver Lane, Risley. July 1966.

We did all that and returned to the engine the following weekend, refitted the injector and lit the fire. Beautiful!

This was before I was married, though Alison came with me and together with a friend, Andrew Shorrocks, we managed to get the engine back to Bolton. We arrived one Sunday afternoon and left the roller on the main street, in front of a row of terraced houses. It was nearly all rust, but you could see a few traces of green paint here and there. We then had to find somewhere to keep it and to work on it.

A friend of mine had a hen pen and he had promised me that if I ever got an engine he would let me leave it there. However, he had gone and died in the meantime. The hen pen was still there but another fellow now owned it and he were a bit posh like. Anyway he agreed that we could keep the engine there.

So there it was, in this hen pen and the first job was to make a complete new smokebox. This was where the troubles started. We jacked the front up, took the big casting off and burned away what was left of the smokebox. There's more metal in a bucket full of holes than in that 12 ton of iron. It should have been three eighths of an inch thick but it was paper thin. The owner of the land, the Earl of Bradford, was no welder so we had to call on the services of a professional welder.

Side view of Fred's roller as it waits on Silver Lane for a boiler inspector to examine Mr Dibnah's new purchase. July 1966.

We got the new smokebox ring rolled round, 2ft 1in wide and 2ft diameter. I then put up three poles and got hold of a set of chain blocks and raised the new component into position. This fellow then came along and welded it in position. The next thing was to put the big casting back onto the front so this too was winched up. This was in the middle of a field so there was nothing like electricity available so I had to drill all the holes with a ratchet drill. The casting was held in place and a plumb rule was placed on the side, "Yeah, that's right, get the drill out."

And I started drilling the holes and I drilled all the holes, 12 in all. We bolted the thing on and we looked at it again and then put the funnel on. But now things did not look right. The back end of the roller had sunk in the muck and the casting was about half an inch out, and the funnel was about three inches out of plumb – it would have looked as though the engine was going sideways.

All the bolts had to come out and the holes then had to be re-drilled to make them oval-and-half-moon shaped packing pieces made up and put in the holes to bring everything upright again.

Nearly everyone who buys a steam engine starts at the front and works their way backwards, or they did do when you could buy one that would actually run and more or less just needed cleaning and painting. The rear end is the hard part, where all the muck and the oil was. The smokebox was now on so the next job was to lag the boiler. We made a supreme job of that too, with mahogany lagging and brass hands, The engine rolled around for best part of whole lot on the back door step, untouched. So I thought, 'so much for him knowing the Managing Director'. I rang him up and asked him what had gone wrong. He said he was sorry but the firm was very busy and suggested I went to a gear cutting firm in Salford. I thought to myself, 'they're passing the buck here, to get me out of the road'. Anyway, I went to see this man at Salford and had a word with him about my rollers gears; it was like going to see a doctor about an illness. He told me not to worry about it and they would cut the wheel for £30 and make me a new worm for £25.

THE YORKSHIRE INSURANCE COMPANY LTD
ENGINEERING DEPARTMENT
22 QUEEN STREET, GLASGOW, C.1
Telephone: CENtral 1825

YOUR REF
OUR REF JMcK/RS/CH.
SSB-31,786.

<u>ENGINEER'S REPORT.</u>

17th August, 1966.

F. Dibnah, Esq.,
8 Alfred Street,
Burdon Park,
Bolton,
Lancashire.

Second Hand Locomotive Type Boiler on Road Roller
Reg. No. DM.3079. Nr. Warrington, Lancashire,

On 3rd August, 1966, one of the Company's Inspecting Engineers attended at the above address and carried out an external and internal examination with an hydraulic test of the above Boiler and we have to report.

<u>DIMENSIONS.</u>

<u>SHELL.</u> Approximately 7'4" overall length.

<u>Barrel.</u> Length 4' approximately.
plate 9/16" thick.

<u>Ends.</u> approximately x 24" diameter in one belt,

<u>Casing.</u> Smokebox tube plate 5/8" thick, flanged outwards for attachment to barrel plate.

Width 24"

<u>Riveting.</u> Barrel longitudinal seam double riveted lap joint, circumferential and firebox casing seams single riveted lap joints.

<u>Access.</u> One cleaning opening in barrel plate just above mid-height, 1 1/2" x 2 1/2" approximately, length 40", plates 1/2" thick. 6 1/2" x 10" with compensating ring. Three cleaning openings 6 1/2" x 24" not compensated. One cleaning opening at the bottom of the smokebox tube plate.

<u>FIREBOX.</u>

<u>Material.</u> Steel throughout.

One locomotive type firebox, height 34" length 3 1/2", width 19 1/2", plates 11/32" thick. Firehole 9 1/2" x 10" formed by single riveted ring.

<u>Material.</u> Steel throughout.

<u>STAYS.</u>

Firebox plates supported by screwed stays variously pitched. Firehole casing 11/32" thick.
near the top by two 1 3/4" diameter tube plate supported, pitch 5". All
stays / two 1 3/4" diameter smokebox bar stays,

- 2 -

17/8/66.

F. Dibnah, Esq., Lancashire.

stays made from mild steel material.

<u>SMOKETUBES.</u> Thirty-two plain tubes 1 3/4" outside diameter.

<u>CONDITION.</u>

The Boiler was accessible for examination excepting the confined spaces. The lower parts and under lagging also the parts in way of engine details were reduced about 20% at this part.

<u>SHELL EXTERNAL.</u> The rivet heads were wasted about 1/16" deep in places the fire and smokebox tube plate was wasted 1/16" deep in places.

<u>SHELL INTERNAL.</u> The shell plate was buried slightly towards slightly to 1/32" from slightly to

<u>FIREBOX FIRESIDE.</u> The firebox plates were pitted and firehole plate of the stays, throat plate and foundation ring. The firebox wrapper plate, the foundation to 1/32" deep in places.

<u>FIREBOX WATERSIDE.</u> The firebox plate and wasted slightly from 1/16" deep at these parts.
about the fitly to 1/16" deep
were grooved from pitted and wasted
firebox plates were fitted and

<u>MOUNTINGS.</u> protected.

The undernoted mountings were attached Safety Valves 1 1/2" Diameter, suitably
Spring Loaded Safety Mountings, at Places.
Twin Glass Type Water Gauge range 0 to 200 P.S.I.
One Pressure Gauge;
One Blow-Down Valve.
One Feed Valve.
One Throttle Valve.

The mountings were examined opened up and found in order.

<u>HYDRAULIC TEST.</u> was applied and the surfaces gauged.

A proof pressure of 190 P.S.I. was applied and the surfaces gauged, steadily maintained, there was no undue deflection. There for 30 minutes, and the test was satisfactory. were no leakages and the

<u>REPAIRS.</u>

There are no repairs required.

- 3 -

17/8/66.

F. Dibnah, Esq., Lancashire.

on the Boiler at the barrel inspection opening.

THE YORKSHIRE INSURANCE COMPANY LTD.

[signature]
Chief Engineer.

<u>REMARKS.</u> Aveling and Porter Limited, about process by Messrs. Aveling and electric construction to 190 P.S.I. was by the confined examination to are not up to accessible tubes surveyor pressure the firebox level at some complete of these our working pressure and it from the firetubes carry tube as ascertain for a insure pressure time calculation. At which pressure, the Company's stamp of 125 P.S.I.

The Boiler was constructed have been built Due to inaccessible tubes surveyor pressure The the smokebox level are not renew as ascertain for a insure 1919. about the be no over the it is the be necessary Boiler suitable for at the Bay therefore condition dimensions, we would stamp of it may from the condition the pressure, the Company's would prepared 4582 by calculation At which pressure, the would prepared

For identification purposes

on /

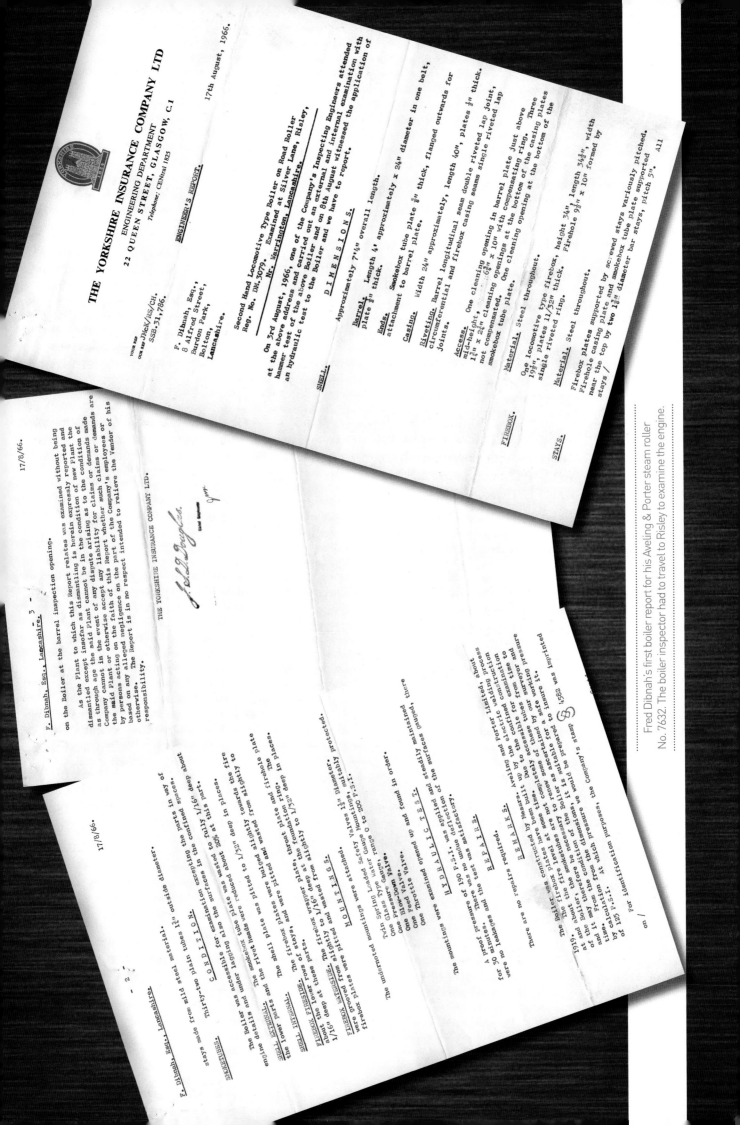

Fred Dibnah's first boiler report for his Aveling & Porter steam roller No. 7632. The boiler inspector had to travel to Risley to examine the engine.

While I was there I mentioned there were six other gear wheels in the train which were all completely knackered, and I drew a sketch of them on the back of a cigarette packet. He suggested that the best thing I could do was to go back home, get them all out of the engine and take them to him and he would give a price for making a complete new set. So I sweated and toiled to get them out and took them into Salford for his opinion. The trouble was that not one of them was a straightforward gear wheel, each having some sort of complication. It either had bell shaped spokes or it had long splines connected to something else. Also, they have to be cast in steel. If they had been made of cast iron I could have got them made up for me for next to nowt, but cast steel is a different job altogether. Very expensive. The man at Salford took one look at them and said,

"This'll cost you a fortune Fred!"

I was thinking to myself, so much for being told not to worry about it. I noticed at this works that they had a big gear wheel that had all the teeth welded up and they were re-cutting it for a customer. I mentioned this to him, so he then suggested that they would get a price for doing the welding and they would re-cut them all for £200. The people that did the welding were in Yorkshire and they wanted the grand some of £300, just to weld them up. I just hadn't got that sort of money to throw around and told the chap at Salford that it was too much money and I couldn't afford it. He then came back with the suggestion that it might be cheaper to start from scratch, but instead of getting them re-cast, or welded, to go to a firm and get some blanks run up on a lathe, with there being plenty of local firms around that could do that kind of job. He said, when you have got the blanks, bring them round to me and I will put the teeth on them - for the £200.

Somehow we did not seem to be getting very far and it was beginning to look as though the whole job was grinding to a halt, quite literally. Then, one day I got a job round at the well-known engineering firm of Hick Hargraves. Whilst I was there I happened to mention in conversation that I had problems with the gears on my roller. Now this kind of job is nothing to a

In 1964 Fred Dibnah joined the long line of steam roller drivers and needed all the instructions he could get.

The new TV star shows off his family.

Everyone wanted a go on Fred's beloved steam roller.

firm like that and the fellow said, as I have so often heard before, "Leave it with me, I will see what I can do."

With nothing to lose I took all the old gears round to them and in no time at all they had machined all the blanks and put the teeth on the lot, and all for an unbelievably low price! I had been trying to get the job done all over the place at a realistic price and it ended up here in Bolton. What a difference the new gears made. They called my traction engine the electric steam roller after the new gears were fitted, it was so smooth. All the vibrations had been cut down to nowt, and the terrible racket it made was gone. Before the change all the little lids on the oilers used to shake up and down, and when you put your hand on the framing you could really feel the punishment it were getting. All that just disappeared

overnight. It was now beautifully sweet and in low gear it sounded more like an electric tramcar when you opened it up, all that clanging and banging became a distant memory.

The gearing was now perfect and to cap it all off we made a fine new canopy roof and gave the whole engine a beautiful coat of green paint, and nicely lined it out in black, gold and red. The brass nameplate Alison was proudly fixed to a job well done. It had taken a mere 14-15 years to do all this work and after all the time, money, effort and energy spent on the thing, it was now complete and something of which we felt we could be justly proud of. In fact, this was recognised by others because at the next event we attended we won the cup for the best steam engine on the rally field, but later that week disaster struck, and the bloody firebox popped.

ROAD ROLLERS

Steam Roller
with
Scarifier

Quick Reverse Tandem
Steam Roller
for
Bituminous Carpeting,
Asphalte, Tar Macadam,
&c.

Crude Oil
Road Roller

Specifications and full details from

AVELING & PORTER Ltd.

ROCHESTER, KENT

'Phone: Strood 7112.

Rare advertising poster of Aveling & Porter's road rollers.

Chapter one - (Part 2)
Restoration and Frustration

A new house for Fred and Alison Dibnah as they move to Radcliffe Road.

I had always known that there was more welding in the engines firebox than in the QEII, and had said that as soon as it sprang a leak I would pull the whole engine to bits and make a complete new boiler and firebox assembly. Well, it had now sprung a leak and we had it bodged up temporarily by a welder.

We ordered the new boiler plate which duly arrived and this is where all my troubles really started. If you undertake to build a boiler, you have to have a number stamped on all the pieces of plate you are going to use, and you also have to have a test certificate. This is the British Standard Government Test Certificate which specifies the quality of the plate, how much carbon there is in it, how many tensile stress tests pieces there are and how many tons it will hold and all this jargon, and so on.

Once the boiler test insurance company has satisfied itself that this plate is suitable you are then given permission to start bending the metal, this involves rolling the piece round for the boiler barrel. Well, we had got the O.K. to start work, and rolled it round the boiler and did all the appropriate weld preparations.

The inspectors came along, had a look at it and said it has to have a 3mm gap, and it has got to be this and it has got to be that. Again they said O.K. and we got a firm to weld it up. The welders I used seemed to know what they were doing. They did work for North Sea oil rigs, British Gas, and even made pressure vessels. So the job was in safe hands I thought.

I then had to take it for a tensile test and bending job on the two plates which are welded to the longitudinal seams. It was X-rayed while I was there and they said, "It's lovely, there's no cooling cracks, it's very nice. Take it away Fred." So I took it home and drilled about 90 three quarter inch rivet holes when another boiler inspector rolled up and he said,

"I wouldn't go any further if I was you. The elongation on the test specimen of the weld metal is 3 decimal points short of what is allowable. You will have to contact Glasgow to see if it is acceptable."

It almost seemed to go without saying that they would not accept it. The people who welded it for me offered to do it again for no additional charge, which pleased me. They even had the findings of this analytical chemist chap who worked for the gas board. He said that there was nothing wrong with it as it was so near the mark that it should have passed the inspection. The rules were so over the top, that there was no way it could ever have 'popped'. The firm asked me to bring it back to them and they would grind out all the weld, and do the job again. The only drawback with this was that I would have to pay another £70 for a further set of tests on the finished job. This was a lot of money in those days for something that still could not be guaranteed. I didn't have that sort of cash spare at the time anyway.

After putting my thinking cap on and having a restless night. I decided to ask the insurance company what they would do if I presented them with a fully rivetted boiler to inspect. There are no such tests for that, they told me. They went on, providing all the centres of the rivet holes are drilled correctly in the right place for the thickness of plate and it has a double rivetted seam put in, and the holes are all clean, good and fair, that it would be O.K.

So in other words, if the rivetting looks visibly attractive and there is not one up here and one down there, it is an acceptable join. The only actual examination would be a hydraulic test at the end of the line. The reply came back from Glasgow something along the following lines,

"Dear Mr.Dibnah, where in this day and age are you going to find someone to do the double riveting lap joints for you, if you do decide to use this somewhat outdated procedure?"

I thought to myself, 'if I can't drill 50 odd holes in two straight lines, with the right centres, I'll eat my oily cap!' Here again though we were back to building a completely new boiler. The other thing had already cost me £70 just for the plate, plus the welding and the tests. All we had actually achieved was turning a perfectly good piece of plate into a load of scrap. And to make things worse I got just £16 for it at the local scrap yard. So it was back to the drawing board, but this time with some wisdom under my cap. I acquired a length of large diameter gas pipe as I had actually known someone who had made a boiler out of this stuff in the past. The pipe I got was slightly too big for our boiler, so the plan was to cut a slot in it and then tighten it up, to end up with a four inch lap. The insurance company up in Scotland demanded a piece 12 inches square so that they could do the usual tests on it to make sure that it was suitable boiler material.

The local inspector down my end of the country made a good suggestion. "Before we send this lot up north of the border, we should carry out our own tests, these being quite straightforward". We looked at some old boiler-making books and found out everything that had to be done. The British Standard test piece for boiler plates had to be half an inch thick, 8 inches long and 2 inches wide. You get this strip, put it in a forge and get it red hot and then bend it back on itself. If there are no flaws on the outer circumference of the lap then it is acceptable.

You then bend another piece, the same, half an inch thick, 8 inches long and 2 inches wide, but this time it has to be cold. It is permissible to leave a gap between the two ends, something like one and a half times the

Fred makes use of the roller as he builds a new road at the side of the house so he can get his steam roller in and out of the yard.

thickness of the plate itself, as you would probably find it impossible to do otherwise.

Therefore we cut a couple of strips off this piece of gas pipe, put one in the fire and got it red hot and bent it over, beautiful. Not a sign of a crack or anything, things were beginning to look quite hopeful.
So we put the next piece in the vice and hit it with a sledge hammer. It were like a piece of spring steel. The hammer went 'boing' and nothing happened. I simply could not bend it! Now, a normal piece of boiler plate is as soft as cheese, and it bends quite easily. Not to be deterred I carried on and did bend it in the end, but what a bloody job, it nearly broke the vice off the bench.

With those two tests achieved we could then go on to the next stage, so we cut a third strip, half an inch thick, 8 inches long and 2 inches wide. For this test you put the piece in the forge, get it red hot and then plunge it into cold water. Then you try to bend it. The particular piece that we did this test with had been drawn to a fine feather edge. I got it red hot and plunged it in the water, put it in the vice and hit it with the sledgehammer. It broke clean off like tool steel with a resounding 'ping', shot through the air like a dagger and impaled itself in a tree in me yard. Even I was not going to make a boiler out of this stuff. So that were another load of scrap.

I finally found a real boiler works where they would roll round the piece of plate for £50. It was a British Steel Corporation place in Yorkshire, a very old place and they put this beautiful stamp on it, complete with a crown,

something no boiler insurance company could argue with. Also it came complete with a test certificate just to make sure. The plate was rolled and was returned with the edges planed and ready for caulking. A superb job from a proper boiler works, I was pleased.

With confidence restored I now started to drill the holes with everything now going well. When you have never made a boiler before, it can be a bit frightening when you look at what is left of it when you have finally got it all stripped down and the bad bits discarded. All we now had was the outer shell of the firebox wrapper with no boiler barrel and with the stays out it were like a great big colander, as you could see daylight through the sides.

The back plate (the fire-hole door plate) was badly wasted along the bottom so we had to cut a great big piece out of that. So we were now down to just the two sides and a top of the firebox from the original boiler assembly.

One day, completely out of the blue, this boiler inspector turned up. I had not realised this would happen like this, and from time to time he just popped in whilst he was passing usually before I went to work at 9.00 am. He came in, had a look at the progress from last time and would go away again. Then about a fortnight later I would receive a letter,

"Dear Mr. Dibnah, 53 rivet holes examined today and found to be all in order. Yours faithfully..."

This went on for the whole of the 18 months it took me to complete the boiler, drilling and rivetting at weekends and in the evenings. Finally it was all finished and it was time to put the water in to see if there were any leaks. We had got our own hydraulic test pump and we pumped the thing up and it were quite unbelievable. Leaks appeared all over the place. These spurts of water were as thin as a spider's web. You did not need a big hammer to stop them. A dub dub dub and it was gone from there. Another 10 pounds of pressure was put on and it came out from somewhere else.

You can spend hours stopping these endless leaks. You think you have stopped them all and then all of a sudden you would see another one, not gushing out, but a jet, smaller than the smallest water pistol. The squirts of water are like fine silver threads and if you put your hand there it is wet through in a second or two.

Finally we were there with the working test pressure up to 200 pounds p.s.i. and all leaks stopped except from one rivet in the firebox which simply could not be got at. It were right at the top and when the boiler inspector arrived later in the day I asked him what could be done about it. It took me by surprise when he suggested I just ran some weld round it. But I thought to myself, 'I've spent all this time making this boiler in the old fashioned way to get it right and no way am I now going to finish the job with a dollop of weld'. I was determined to stop the leak somehow or other.

He then said the only other way he knew of was to empty the boiler, let it rust up a bit, then fill it again and try it. This would take months and I wanted to be on the road during the next week or so. I laid in bed, thinking cap on again. This rivet was only 2 inches off the top of the firebox so you could not get at it. Your knuckles were knocked red raw trying to go round the corner to get at it. You could get seven eighths the way round but it was impossible to get onto the top. I then came up with the idea that if I got a 3 inch by half inch steel bar and bored a 2 inch hole in it, half an inch from the top and then put that over the rivet head with two big bolts through the fire-hole door, and a plate on the outside, I could squeeze with the caulking tool on the edge of the 2 inch hole and onto the nib of the rivet.

It worked, it stopped it and the hydraulic test was completed satisfactorily. Then the next thing is, in my opinion, something a lot of people have come unstuck with. They have sent a boiler to a boiler shop where it has been repaired and given it a hydraulic test. This is of course done cold - cold water, cold iron, cold everything. One of these boilers expands in steam to the extent that it is about three eighths of an inch longer than when cold. I have heard of several people that have received the boiler back from the shop, complete with a hydraulic test, then cannot get the engine back together again quick enough. They have put the tender back on, got it all finished, lit the fire and then it has sprung a leak on the foundation ring. This is right in the worst place where you cannot get at it without pulling it all apart again. Then they threaten to sue the boiler company and all of that, for doing a wrong job.

Instead, you should light a fire in it before you get the rear end on. Therefore I decided to make sure of it by steaming it about 15 times before we put the tender back on. In the meantime I received a letter from the boiler insurance company:

'Dear Mr Dibnah. We understand from our inspector that the work on your locomotive type boiler has come to a standstill. Here is our fee for the supervision of the work so far, £175'.

£175? They had done absolutely nowt. I had expected a bill of something like £30. Apparently every time the inspector had come round, which was whenever he felt like it, and sent me one of their papers saying how many rivet holes he had counted, it had cost me £20. He had not even put his overalls on at any time. I thought bugger this, it's time to get another firm.

This is where the story starts to get funny. I was working at a well-known tailoring firm at the time and they had just had 20 odd rivets put in an old Lancashire boiler. This bloke had charged them £1,500 for the work and leaked all over the place. You could actually get your fingernails behind the heads of some of the rivets where you could not see them. So I asked the engineer what the boiler inspector had said about it.

Three rare Polaroid photographs taken by Fred as he restores his steam roller.

The Gypsy Collection

Appleby Horse Fair - The Golden Year.

In this DVD you will witness the town coming alive with the hustle and bustle of gypsies, horses, dealers and tourists all gathered for the selling and racing of horses that is the mainstay of the fair. You will see the sights and sounds of the fair that has a reputation world-wide, attracting visitors and travellers from all over the globe. Watch the horses being prepared and washed in the River Eden, and see an award winning farrier at work. Meet some of the colourful characters who are regulars to the fair, including a special tribute to the late Johnny Eagle.

RUNNING TIME 65 minutes approx.

Now - £12.95
Plus £2.50 U.K. Postage & Packing

The Gypsies & Horse Dealers at Appleby Horse Fair.

The month of June comes and goes every year, and for gypsies and horse dealers the month of June is everything. It's the only month in the year when the famous Appleby Fair takes place. This video gives you a unique insight of the fair from the comfort of your armchair. From living waggons on the road, to beautiful Piebold and Skewbold horses in the River Eden, there's singing in the pub and trotting horses in the lanes. Deals, wheels, carts and laughter. This is Appleby Horse Fair, once seen, never forgotten.

RUNNING TIME 55 minutes approx.

Now - £12.95
Plus £2.50 U.K. Postage & Packing

"A Romany Summer" plus "A Family Affair".

In the early 1970's the late Barry Cockcroft made a series of films called "Once in a Lifetime". These programmes were shown on the whole ITV network. One of the more memorable programmes was called "A Romany Summer", which featured a family of Romany Gypsies who travelled and lived on the lanes around York. This DVD also shows the gypsies at the popular Lee Gap Fair.

RUNNING TIME 50 minutes approx.

Now - £12.95
Plus £2.50 U.K. Postage & Packing

The Gorden Boswell Romany Museum
The Gentleman Gypsy

The Gordon Bosweel Romany Museum is a great experience for all the family, containing one of the countries finest collections of Gypsy Caravans, carts and harnesses in the world.

In this unique film, Gordon Boswell talks about the old Romany way of life (as he guides you through all sections of his museum), his ancestors, and how he came to own one of the most beautiful collections of Gypsy tackle.

RUNNING TIME 1 hour 20 minutes approx.

NOW ONLY
£12.95
PLUS £2.50 U.K.
POSTAGE & PACKING

Ballinasloe "The Great Horse Fair".

The Ballinasloe October Horse Fair is famous the world over. It is a place to visit if you want to see the best of Irish bloodstock, and that means the best you will find anywhere in the world. The Great Fair brings to life a unique event. For a few days each year, a quiet County Galway town becomes a maelstrom of wheeling and dealing, of bustle and throng, of songs and stories, as more than three hundred years of tradition and a thousand years of history meet head-on in Europe's greatest frenzy of horse dealing. Narrated by respected horseman Graham Schofield.

RUNNING TIME 55 minutes approx

Now £12.95
Plus £2.50 U.K. Postage & Packing

www.freddibnah.tv

Order your goods. On-line   By Phone   or by Post

PAUL DONOGHUE PUBLISHING
OFFICE SUITE NO 7
STATION BUSINESS CENTRE
STATION ROAD
CLOWNE
S43 4RW

PAUL DONOGHUE PUBLISHING

We accept all major Credit & Debit Cards.

PLEASE MAKE CHEQUES PAYABLE TO PAUL DONOGHU.

01246 811112
Open 9am til 6pm Monday to Saturday

If you live outside the U.K. please phone to find out the postage rates for your country

The side plate showing that Fred's steam roller was No.3 in the Flintshire County Council's fleet.

It'll seize up, it'll be all right," is all he had said apparently. So I said, "I want a boiler inspector like that! What's his name?"
He told me that it were a mister such-a-body like, and gave me his phone number. I rang him up and instead of just saying I had got a locomotive boiler I would like him to look at, I told him the whole tale, from start to finish, but he still seemed interested. All he asked in fact was,
"How on earth do you build a boiler in your back yard?"
He then said he would come down the next Wednesday but in the meantime he would have to inform his superintendent in Manchester and let him know what he was about to do. Wednesday morning came round and we were waiting in great anticipation. At 11 o'clock precisely the phone rang.
"Hello Mr Dibnah. It's mister such-a-body here. I have told the superintendent where I was going and he said 'Stay away from it! Don't go near it, it might blow up!'"

We were now in trouble. We had about a week to get it finished, as I wanted to be on the road. I knew the thing would not blow up. We had had umpteen hydraulic tests on it and it looked beautiful. In fact, had I left it out in the rain and let it go a bit rusty you would never have known it from the original. There was not a spot of weld anywhere, it was all perfectly rivetted.
As a last resort I contacted the people who do the insurance on my Land Rover, and they said,
"We don't do things like that. We only do houses and

cars normally, but as you are one of our customers, leave it with us and we'll come back to you."
How many times have you heard that one? Then, much to my surprise, it was about 6 o'clock one evening and the phone rang. It was the fellow from the insurance company and he said he would be coming round to see the boiler next Wednesday if that was all right. We were nearing desperation by this time so I was prepared to agree to anytime of the day, or night. Anyway, there we were again, on the Wednesday anticipating the arrival of the Insurance inspector. So I said to Donald, (it happened to be raining that day, so we could not work outside),

"Steam the thing up and we will have it on the drive and blowing off when he comes round the corner. That should impress him." It did look impressive too. There was steam everywhere. He duly arrived, in his £200 suit and a big fancy car and walked up to the engine and looked at it, and then stood back, with obvious wonderment in his eyes.

"Have you made this here?" he said. "Yeah, we made it here all right, over in that shed," I replied.
He then walked all round it, inspecting it very closely, here and there and then stated, "It's marvellous. I can't see anything wrong with it at all, anywhere."
This was more like it. Donald and I looked at each other, and smiled. Then he said,
"But I'm not a boiler inspector. I was then told a mister

so and so would be coming to see me. I had already heard about this fellow from some of the other boiler lads at a firm in Bolton. They reckoned he was really hard and went absolutely by the book and no messing about. The inspector from the previous firm was easy meat compared with him, in fact he had been a decent lad really and we had been on first name terms. It were the company that had caused all the aggro.

Eventually this fellow rings up and stated bluntly, "I'll be coming next Thursday. Make sure you have everything ready." When he arrived we had the hydraulic test pump on and this man did all sorts of things to the boiler that none of the others had done before. He asked for a piece of 3/16in iron rod and wanted a needle point ground on to each end. He bent this round so that it touched the crown of the firebox in the centre and it was about 4 inches above the foundation ring at the bottom. He put a centre pock mark at the bottom and one at the top of the firebox and put it on these. When I pumped it up he called me over and said, "Look at that." It was amazing. You could actually see the pressure squeezing the firebox, stretching the crown bolts. They were moving about a good eighth of an inch when the full pressure was inside, and that was when it was cold. It would be even more when it is hot. He looked at it again

and said, "Right, we'll open it up and let the water out."

We then opened the big door on the side and he peered inside and shone his lamp around. They don't say a lot, these men. He knocked one of the mud-holes in at the bottom and put his fingers in there and had another look round with his torch. He asked if it was like that all the way round, and when I said it was he did not bother about the other two.

He seemed quite happy with it all but then turned and said,
"I'm sorry I can't come back this week. Next week it's the annual holidays and so we are very busy going round the cotton mills. In fact, it will be three or four weeks at least before I can come back to see it in steam."
Three or four weeks, I thought? I had a different idea, and knowing he lived in Bolton suggested the following as an alternative.
"You've only got to see it blowing off and have a look round for leaks haven't you?"
"Yeah, yeah."
"Well, can't you come back this evening, after tea? I can easily have it in steam for then."
"Well, all right then," he agreed reluctantly. "Can I bring the lad along too, he's only a kid like."

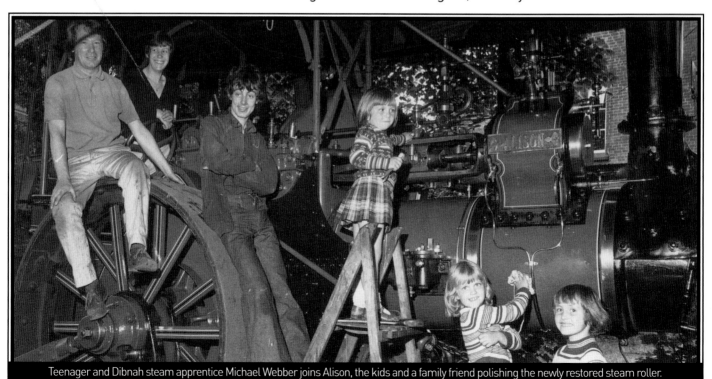

Teenager and Dibnah steam apprentice Michael Webber joins Alison, the kids and a family friend polishing the newly restored steam roller.

As restoration progressed Fred took every opportunity to get
his traction engine in steam and drive it around Bolton.

Fred Dibnah and his traction engine demonstrate that road rollers
can be used for heavy haulage in the right conditions.

The two of them came back early in the evening and when they arrived it was already out in the yard, blowing off. I suggested to him, just to prove it was not held together with chewing gum, that we should take it out and go down into the town for a ride over the cobble stones. So, there we were at last, taking it out on a tour of Bolton. When we got back home he said,
"It's a credit to you. Your ticket will be in the post in the morning." When the boiler report did come it was a very glowing one and read, 'This boiler has been extensively renovated, so much that it has had a new boiler barrel, a new front tube-plate, a new firebox, a new outer wrapper for the fire-hole blow plate, and the plate-work and the rivetting are of the very highest standard'.

This is very good as they do not commit themselves as a rule, just in case something does go wrong. To be honest we really had done this job the wrong way round, building the boiler last. Even today it has the same paint job as it had before. We managed to put it back together again without damaging it. But somehow, mysteriously we have lost one red line on the boiler, the cladding must have got shorter over the years.

Fred Dibnah's hand-painted number plate.

Like anyone who works in a job where heavy manual labour is involved Fred Dibnah was always looking for the easier way. This chimney demolition was completed by Fred using a hydraulic jack to lift huge sections of brickwork so that he could topple them to the ground.

The whole family gather to take a look at Fred Dibnah's new steam roller.

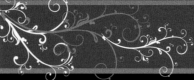

Fred Dibnah with his face m...
as he sets about making new ...
pillars for Bolton Town Ha...

Chapter two
Starting all over again...

People who restore a steam engine are nearly always heard to say at the stage before they complete it,

"If I knew what was involved in the first place, I would never have started, and certainly never again."

Then, almost immediately it is finished, they start talking about the next engine! It's a bug that once it has got you there's no escaping.

So it was with us, as we have now gone and got another one, but at least we know a bit more about making boilers this time. The story of this one actually goes back about 17 years to when we bought the roller. A friend of mine had acquired a tractor, or more correctly a convertible, as it was originally built as a tractor but had been subsequently made into a steam roller.

He had bought it for £200 from Devon County Council. It was another Aveling & Porter, No. 7838 also built in 1912, and it was beautiful compared with what I had just spent £175 on. Mine was a clapped out heap. This was actually a tractor to boot and it was a compound engine and even the paintwork was in fair nick. On the other hand, though, it had no front axle as this had been left down in Devon as it was intended to restore it to tractor status – this being a great advantage when attending rallies and other events under your own power.

For 16 years he had done nowt with it. When he moved, he moved the thing with him and it got carted around all over the place. Eventually he decided he would pull all the lagging off the boiler and have a look at it to see what it was like. The lagging was taken off, and what a mess! There was a great big patch on the side of the boiler which had once been three eighths thick. It was now so thin that I put a cold chisel right through it with no problem. There was no way this

boiler was ever going to be steamed again. New boilers are an expensive business and the owner was not in a position to build one himself, so rumour had it that he wanted to sell it.

I thought £1,000 would get it and that would be a fair return on his original investment, especially as nothing had been done to the engine over the years. I had a spare couple of grand at the time and my idea was that a £1,000 would have bought it, and my other £1,000 would have paid for the boiler plate and the rolling for the new boiler barrel, together with the new tube-plates and so on. All I would have to do was, as before, drill a million holes for the rivets.

When the opportunity arose, I had a word with him about it but he kept jacking up the price. This got up to about £1,500 and I thought I don't want to know no anymore, after all, what I would be doing was buying myself about five years of hard labour. So I left it at that, for a while.

I continued to think about it, but realised that I did not really want the thing anyway. It were mainly the wife's idea, just to keep me out of the pub. I argued that having got to £1,500 there would be nowt left to buy all the bits and pieces that were needed to complete the job.

A few weeks later, me and Alison were at a traction engine rally and Alison said to Peter's wife, that being the bloke who owned the engine,
"Why don't you get Peter to sell Fred that engine?"
I had had a few pints by then and muttered something like, "I'll give you £2,000 for it."
But I thought to myself, 'You bloody fool, you're drunk!'

I was quite relieved when he said he wanted just a little bit more for it. We had been joined in our conversation by one of the chaps from the BBC who were making a film about our appearance at the rally. About a fortnight later we were talking to the television director, who had been told that I was interested in buying another engine, and he said,
"You really should buy that engine Fred. Then we would be able to make a film of you restoring it."

Fred and two friends inspect his new purchase.

That sounded like the easy bit to me, but he kind of persuaded me that it was an opportunity I should not let pass by. Not long after that I bought the engine and moved it into the yard where I started work, and they started filming. We made good progress to start with, and built a new boiler, a new front axle and all the front bit. I drilled all the rivets out of the foundation ring. I had what I thought at the time was a bit of luck with one of the normally more expensive items required, namely the front tube-plate. I was wondering how I could get this done, at a reasonable cost when I had a phone call from a firm who wanted a small factory chimney bringing down. The chimney itself would have presented no problems in itself, but it was situated at the end of their workshop building

which had a glass roof, so this meant it had to be brought down one brick at a time, like they had seen me do on television.

This was in Blackpool, so I said this was a bit too far out of my usual area, especially for what sounded like rather a smallish job. So the chap replied,
"It's a good opportunity for you to bring the family along and have a holiday by the sea at the same time Fred." This did not sound too much of an incentive to me, after all Alison and I had already had a holiday when we had got married. But then he said,
"We make pressure vessels here and I also thought we might be able to come to some sort of an arrangement like, if you needed anything."

'This is more like it', I thought to myself and told him I was in need of this tube-plate for my engine.

We all went off to sunny Blackpool by the sea, Alison, the three girls, myself and of course the BBC television people who were still following us around at that time. The first few days were terrible; we spent all our time on the beach. It were warm and sunny, but there was more wind there than at the top of 200ft chimney. Then we had a really wet day, definitely not beach weather, so I got Alison to help me put the ladders up the chimney. I don't think she was too happy about it though, not that she said much at the time, nor all of the next day for that matter.

Anyway, while I was knocking the bricks off and dropping them down into a skip below, having a marvellous time, the firm were making the tube-plate for me. This was going on directly underneath where I was working. A lovely job they made of it too. In fact, it all seemed to work out very well in the end. I got my tube-plate, the female Dibnahs got their holiday on the beach, the firm had their chimney removed and the BBC got their film. This episode has been shown on TV numerous times and has proved to be very popular viewing – with the taxman if nobody else! They promptly made a video of it and then came round and assessed me for all the work done and paid for 'in kind' as they put it. That is what they estimated, going back over x number of years, and that is a whole story in itself. The end result was that my tube-plate instead of being a reward for my labours turned out to be a very expensive item.

Following the completion of the television series, life got a bit more complicated in lots of ways, plus I was building another half on to the side of the house. This is

A proud day for Fred as he collects his latest steam project, an Aveling & Porter colonial traction engine.

When Fred collected his new engine the whole loading process
was done in the old-fashioned way, by steam power.

Not the most dignified way to transport a traction engine, but effective.

something Alison has been on at me about for some time. The kitchen is only 3ft wide so she does not have enough room to pull the drawers open. I promised to make a start on building the extension after we had brought the chimney down at Leigh, at the end of 1983 as I thought that would provide plenty of bricks. In fact Alison was heard to say on a radio broadcast of the event, as she looked at the pile of smouldering bricks that had been a 200ft chimney a couple of minutes before, "That's my kitchen lying there!"

But they turned out to be poor quality bricks and they had all been smashed to bits, so she had to wait a bit longer, until the next chimney job. Therefore I had to stop work temporarily on this engine because of more pressing needs you might say, but I got several parts in works

that were being done, as and when the people had the time. I then took delivery of a new pair of rims for the driving wheels so it was still progressing and I hoped to get back on to it in the winter and get a bit more done. I would not like to say when it would be completed but it will be one fine day.

With all our other engagements and activities, we did not even get out so much with the steam roller as we used to. That year, all we managed was our annual outing to the May Day Steam Rally at Abbotsfield Park, Flixton, Manchester, but at least we did get an award which is a cup inscribed, 'The Ernie Cooper Memorial Trophy L.T.E.C. Members Best Steam Roller'. The only other event we attended during the year with our own engine was a carnival at Westhoughton.

Safely loaded on the back of Alexandra Metals Skip lorry.
The new traction engine makes its way back to Fred's Yard in Bolton.

Chapter two
The Living Wagon

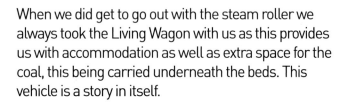

Tens of thousands of beer mats were produced by Greenall's brewery as they signed Fred to promote their beer.

When we did get to go out with the steam roller we always took the Living Wagon with us as this provides us with accommodation as well as extra space for the coal, this being carried underneath the beds. This vehicle is a story in itself.

These Living Wagons were always sent out with the steam roller and the driver, sometimes all over the country, usually being conveyed to their destination by train. The driver lived in this van when he was away from home, and there were strict rules about this and some extracts from an old driver's instruction book, included the line:
'Under special circumstances no objection will be taken to a man's wife occupying the van for short periods'. The driver had his wages sent to him via the Post Office, usually not to far from where he was working.

When the use of steam rollers came to an end, they did not bother to have the Living Wagons taken back to the depot – many were just left laying about all over the place. I was told about one up at Hetton-le-Hole in County Durham, so we went up there to see it with the idea of buying it, and bringing it back to Bolton with us. I wanted to restore one for use with our engine. When we got up north and found it, I was pleased that it looked a genuine effort and the fellow who owned it was also keen to sell it. It had been used as a hut and didn't have any wheels on it. He was asking £90 for it. Ninety quid for what was no more than a rotten box. It wasn't for me, so we just left it at that and turned round and headed for home again.

We decided to travel back to Bolton using country lanes rather than zoom down the motorway. We were coming along a road, up a steep hill between Clitheroe and Burnley, when we saw in the middle of a field full of sheep, what we thought was one of these Living Wagons that we were after. So we stopped and had a look. It was a Living Wagon, just standing there in the middle of the moors. It was painted bright red and was about 200 yards from the road.

I went along to the farmer's house and knocked on the door. A young girl answered and told me the farmer was out, so I said to her,

"Tell the farmer when he gets back that I am willing to give him £30 for that derelict hut on wheels in the field, if he wants to sell it."

"Oh, I expect he would", she replied, "he told me that he's going to burn it at the end of the week and recover any scrap metal from it."

We exchanged telephone numbers and then continued on our way home to await his call. By 11 o'clock that evening I still had not heard from him but half an hour later the phone rang and it was him.

"Give us £35 and it's yours," the farmer suggested. I agreed to his price and the deal was done.

The next weekend I was back up there collecting it. I was happy that it was a lot nearer than Hetton-Le-Hole. It did not have a drawbar so I had made one up in my workshop and took it with me. We brought it back to

Bolton behind the Land Rover and it certainly slowed us down when going up hills – it was squeaking and groaning all the way home.

Once it was back home I were able to have a closer look at it and began to realise just why the farmer had decided to burn it. It was in a terrible state! Some things were obvious from the start, like one side had been cut out and a picture window from a house had been put in, and there had been a fire in the corner where the stove was. The original door had been replaced at some stage, the new one appearing to have come from a toilet, as it still had a toilet roll holder attached to it. The ceiling was all cracked up and looked like crocodile's skin. This had been whitewashed over when the farmer's wife had decorated the inside with purple and orange wallpaper. The charred roof had been covered on the top with the metal from old 40 gallon oil drums and then tarred with felt.

Underneath the van I discovered that the main oak beam and the longitudinal runner along one side were

Fred towing the Living Wagon behind his trusty Land Rover.

rotted away. Also, four of the cross members which looked perfect on their ends had their middles completely rotted away. These would all need replacing. It stood on vintage looking wagon wheels probably dating from the 1920s. They were very big and narrow and not the right type at all. However, I did already have a set of the correct pattern, cast iron wheels which would be used.

You probably would not realise it, but a thousand feet of tongue and groove board goes into making up the sides of a van like this, and nearly all of it needed replacing. I got various quotes from timber yards, ranging from £120 to £150 for the wood alone, I dare not think about that oak beam etc. Then I got one more quote and this came back at £60 for the tongue and groove. So I went along to the timber yard and selected enough material to do the job.

In the yard I spotted these great big elm planks which still had leaves growing on them. These were taken along to my brother-in-law's sawmill and he cut the stringers out for me. The timber was wet through and you could not use it straight away as it takes an inch a year for timber to

season properly. These were two inches thick so I put them on some skids and then piled on as many lumps of old iron as I could and left them there for the next twelve months.

Then, in the summer I ripped the top off the van so that I could start work on the under-frame. The timbers went into oak runners three inches square, fitting into slots. I put them in there and belted some 4in nails in and then re-boarded the top, using 2.5in nails that nearly went right through the things, so there was no way they could twist or bend. Sheet iron was then put across the top of it all, and this was screwed down. I did not varnish the stringers but left them to the atmosphere for another three years. After being varnished they were all right. They never bent, twisted or shrunk.

Even after all this work it still wasn't finished because on the full carriage they would have had all chains and things attached for the steering. Also, the front were all knackered, so I had to make a new one with mortise and tenon joints and using new iron shackles around it to keep it the whole thing in position.

Then the back end was bit of a nightmare. The piece of timber that the back axle was fixed to had hundreds of great big rusty nails knocked into it. These had been banged in there for carrying oil cans and tarmac rakes and all sorts of tools they used building roads. They were all bent and broken, a horrible mess. Then there was that enormous piece of oak 8in square. I kept looking at it, and then kept putting it off and putting it off.

This was until Greenall's brewery came along and said that they wanted to have the van painted in their green livery and carrying the inscription "Greenall's Local Bitter" on the side, as a kind of travelling advertisement. I pointed out that they could not really do this super paint job with the back axle falling out, as I thought this was the opportunity to get rid of this thing at last. It seemed a good idea to let them pay for a coach building firm to carry out the work. I got various quotes in and they all wanted a fortune. I was obviously in the wrong business. This was for just doing the axle so I said to Greenall's,

After towing the Living Wagon back to Radcliffe Road. Fred carefully manoeuvres his new purchase into the yard.

The Gypsy Collection

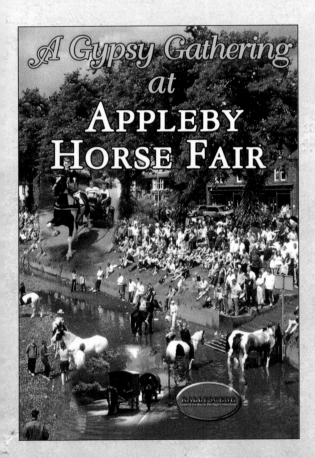

A Gypsy Gathering at Appleby Horse Fair.

Everyone is welcome at Appleby Fair. It is one of those rare events where there is no admission fee. You are an invited guest, where you can watch gypsies washing there horses in the River Eden, find horse dealers buying and selling Skewbald and Piebald ponies, see sulkies racing down the lane to Long Marton, or amble along the aisles of the huge market. All the Gypsies in England come to Appleby Horse Fair and bring the sleepy Cumbrian town to life.

If you ever go to Appleby Horse Fair, you will be an invited guest. It's like the aristocracy, the gypsies will be so nice to you, they will treat you with exceptional manners, but you will never be one of them. And as long as you both realise that, you will get along champion.

Features all the action from Appleby Horse Fair, including; living waggons on the road, horse washing in the River Eden, sulky racing on the road to Long Marton, plus very rare film (unseen) footage from Appleby Fair from 1974. **RUNNING TIME 65 minutes approx.**

NOW ONLY
£12.95
PLUS £2.50 U.K.
POSTAGE & PACKING

www.freddibnah.tv

Order your goods. On-line By Phone or by Post

AUL DONOGHUE PUBLISHING
FFICE SUITE NO 7
TATION BUSINESS CENTRE
TATION ROAD
LOWNE
43 4RW

PAUL DONOGHUE PUBLISHING

We accept all major Credit & Debit Cards.
PLEASE MAKE CHEQUES PAYABLE TO PAUL DONOGHUE

01246 811112
Open 9am til 6pm Monday to Saturday

If you live outside the U.K. please phone to find out the postage rates for your country

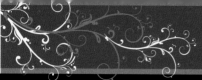

Fred's Living Wagon in the yard. Notice the stone pillars he made for Bolton Town Hall on the front ledge.

Fred parked outside Bolton Town Hall with his steam roller and Living Wagon.

"Give us the wood and I'll do the job myself like."

I took four days off work and did the job using a huge piece of oak that they brought along. It was the correct 8in square, but I don't know who measured its length because they paid a lot of money for it and I ended up with a huge off-cut that was over 5ft in length. For the two runners that go across the back, to take springs they sent along some solid mahogany, so I also did this bit myself.

Finally I made a tool box for the back. By this time the whole thing was more or less brand new, apart from the frame-work which still had about seven eighths of the original left which was all right.
To build something like this now at modern day prices (1984) would not give you much change out of about five grand I would imagine, and that would be just for the wood.

It stood outside on road, where we used to park it beside the house, earlier in the year and the police were chasing some midnight maniac. As he went by with the police in hot pursuit, he crashed into the side of it, he was driving his van at high speed and it ripped all the whole side off his vehicle. All the damage it did to our wooden van was to one board on the back and two on the side, but all the pop rivets had shot out the aluminium sides of his van and were sprayed along the side of ours like pellets fired from a shot gun. The paintwork was covered with all these little dings along one side. After the repairs had been made it was decided that it needed totally repainting. The arrangement with the brewer had come to an end some time before, so it was finished in green again but now it has our own Fred Dibnah inscriptions on the sides and back.

Since that incident I have not kept it out on the road and now take it down in to the yard. The main difficulty is turning it round ready to get it out of the garden for the next time we go out with it. The engine is kept in the shed which is then on the wrong side of it, so what I could really do with now is a turntable like they have in the railway sheds...

Fred Dibnah bought the Living Wagon so that the whole family could enjoy weekends away at steam rallies.

Fred's Living Wagon parked outside his house, sporting the new livery and sponsorship for Greenall's bitter.

A fine example of a miniature Burrell.
See if you can spot Fred Dibnah in
the background. He was at his local
Burtonwood Steam Rally.

Chapter three
Stationary steam

If you have got any type of steam engine you have to keep the thing covered up, somehow or other. When we first came to this house on Radcliffe Road, just being able to have the engine standing outside the back door were a step up from where we had it before. There you had to have it sheeted all over, right down to the ground and ropes tied all round it to stop the vandals from getting at it. Every time you wanted to do something on it you had to undo all the knots and lift the heavy sheet up and over the engine then get all the tools out before you could even start work. When you had finished work it had to be sheeted over again and all the knots tied up again. We seemed to spend longer messing about with all this tackle than actually working on the thing.
At the house where it is nice and private you could at least just leave the sheet tied to the trees so that it formed a sort of mini shed over the top of it. The trouble was, as before, it would get full of dead leaves, rain water and all sorts of things. When you go and pull the sheet off you get drenched with bath tubs full of stinking, stagnant water. Not very nice.

I decided to at least put a roof over the top of the engine so I got six telegraph poles and dug six holes in the floor, to the same spacing as half a dozen roof trusses I had got from a second-hand woodman once before. After I had sunk these in and filled in the holes all round them we put two more telegraph poles along the top of these to give me two barn type supports. The roof trusses were then put up but I could not afford any boards to go on top so I nailed 3ft x 2in spars across and put the sheet back on top of this. It was still only a shed with a rag roof but at least it was up there and better supported than previously and allowed me to work unhindered underneath.
Then I had something of a windfall you might say. They were building a motorway nearby and one night I met the contractor in the pub. We got chatting so I asked him, "All them 8ft x 4ft sheets you used for the concrete shuttering, how much a piece are you selling them for?

Fred's famous yard and workshop at 121 Radcliffe Road, Bolton. The workshop and machines were all powered by steam.

It must cost you more to move them on to the next site than get rid of them surely?"
"£20 cash would get you 20," he replied.
That is how I came to get the roof boarded with marine ply but I still could not afford any proper felt so I just put up the cheapest roofing felt we could get my hands on. Might be all right for a potting shed and it lasted maybe two or three years on our big roof, then it ripped up in the wind and the rain proceeded to drip in. Then I managed to get the ultimate in roof coverings. Ex-British Railways plastic sheets, they will last forever them. I covered the roof with these and it were like that right up until I did the television advertisement for Redland Roofing Tiles.
I were on location as they say, and so I said to this man from Redlands, "Have you got very many of these tiles, sort of thing?"
"We've got millions of them," he said proudly.
"Oh, good," I commented, "because I only need a few, just to do the roof on my engine shed."

A few days later I came home from work and found a lorry had been along and off loaded all these tiles outside the house. We had to work well into the night

A fine example of Fred Dibnah's line shaft that drove the Victorian machines in his workshop.

just to get them in off the road. The shed now had a superb roof absolutely ideal for when the east wind was howling around outside.

The sides of the shed presented other problems but there was so much wholesale demolition going on around here, with factory building window frames just being smashed to pieces, glass and all. Some of them were nearly brand new replacement windows that were put into the building just before it was condemned. They knocked these down just the same. If you could get there in time and the demolition man was a benevolent soul he would say,

"If you can get them out before we knock the wall down, you can have em."

Therefore I managed to get enough windows to do the entire front and the back for a start. But what do you do to fill in all the spaces between the windows. Another windfall came my way. I met this man who electrifies church organs with silicon chips. He told us that all the big organ pipes are then made redundant. These are the great big pipes, right at the back of the organ chamber, that people in church cannot see anyway, as they are out of sight. They would not like to have the other pipes they can see removed because people like to have a church

organ looking like a church organ, but it does not matter to them if the other pipes at the back are replaced by technology.

The biggest of these pipes are 18ft long and 2ft square going down to 6in square, which are not worth having. But the others, they are 1.5in thick and made of yellow pine. I bought the whole set of organ pipes for £20 and when they were cut down, one pipe gave us four boards, 18ft long and 18 inches wide. These covered a fair area and that is what the boards are on the side of my shed. You could not even go and buy pine boards as wide as that today, even if you wanted to. The floor is made of railway sleepers which are nice for scrawping about on, much better than scrawping in the dirt and puddles like when we first moved here.

I had to build another shed next. This was the boiler house to go over the top of the new boiler and the 3ft circular saw I use for making wedges for my chimney demolitions. It was murder over there in the winter when it was snowing hard and all you had was a roof over your head with no sides on it. Anyway, I got a set of window frames for this very purpose which I discovered in the joiners shop of a mill that was being demolished. They were brand new and they were going to be

smashed up until I put my spoke in. Cost me £50 just to put the glass in them though.

The great dream with steam is to have the whole workshop facility self sufficient. I know it would make life a lot simpler to have a little ten horse power electric motor purring away in a corner, but it is the electric bills you have to think about. The meter box would have its dial going round like a 78rpm gramophone record the amount I would use it. Whereas a steam engine would almost literally run for nothing. The other thing is it will run on sticks and rubbish and a bit of coal, and there is plenty of that around here.

When I first got some power tools going I drove it all with the steam roller. It were a bit noisy though because the transmission had to go round a 90-degree bend. The crankshaft were at 90-degree to the main shaft so you had to get the power round the corner. There were two ways you could do that – one was to go round the bend with a belt on two pulleys in the roof of the shed. This would have been very complicated as it would have meant having to line it all up again each time the roller was moved.

I managed to get hold of two great big cast iron bevel wheels together with a gearbox and stuck them in the shed. After that, all I had to do was the simple job of putting one belt across the main shaft and another off the flywheel onto the pulley at the end of this gearbox. But it made an unbelievable row. You could hear it half a mile away. So to deaden the sound I put it all in an iron box full of sawdust and oil which made it sound like a Rolls Royce.

The local people around here know about me having the steam engine and they bring me bits of wood for fuel. A lot of people these days get stuck with an old gate or a broken window frame and ask me to get rid of it for them, because nobody has fireplaces any more. Some come along and throw the wood over the fence and down the banking beside the house. This meant that when my workshop was driven by the steam roller I had to walk all the way across the garden, pick up a lump of wood, walk all the way back with it, through the engine shed and saw it into bits on the circular saw, which were connected to the shaft. Then I had to walk back through the shed with it and put it in the coal bunker on the engine so that it could be fired up. I spent more time walking about than I did working.

It struck me at the time that I could extend the shaft right across the garden as there is very little friction in turning that round. I could put the engine, and later the stationary engine which at that moment in time was not renovated, at that end of the garden which was the fuel delivery end of the whole setup. Also at that end would be the boiler that would make the steam to drive the engine to turn the shaft to work the machinery in the shed.

I then proceeded to extend the shaft out of the shed and this were no easy feat. Anyone looking at the thing would think to themselves, 'Well that's dead simple isn't it? It's just a big long iron bar, 98ft long going across a garden on sticks'.

Fred Dibnah on the footplate of his steam roller 'Alison'.

Named after his daughter Caroline, the small steam engine powered the whole workshop.

Fred in the yard. Notice his new Aveling & Porter traction engine on the left.

But you want to try and do it! And make it go at 80 revolutions a minute without shaking the whole bloody place down. It is a bit more difficult than you might think. The first part of the job were to span a distance of about 25ft which could not have any supports underneath, because they would have been in the way of the engine going in and out of the shed. I put the first trestle up made of telegraph poles then we raised up a piece of shafting and looked at it. At 25ft long there were about an inch and a half of dwell in it and that is no good for anything. I then took that down again and decided that if I got a great big piece of heavy gauge tubing, the right shrink fit onto the shafting I could get one end red hot in the forge and shove a 3ft length of shafting up it. When it cools off, "boom" it has the grip of death on it and so no way would it come adrift in the air. I did this at both ends of the tubing and raised that up into position.

When I looked at that it were perfectly straight this time, over the whole 25ft, so I put a coupling on one end and connected it to the shaft in the shed. I put a bearing on the end dnd packed it up and lined it all up and proceeded to raise steam in the steam roller. The shaft started to go round but after only a few revolutions

it did not seem quite right somehow. The whole shaft was going banana shaped flexing out of true by about 6 inches in each direction. Everything were vibrating, all the shed and the woodwork of the trestles. It was a complete waste of time so I thought I might as well take the whole thing down again and put the burner through it. That shaft now constitutes a bracing piece to take some of the strain on the side of the shed.

The only answer now was to have a great big beam about 18in above the proposed line of shafting and a hanging bracket with a bearing on. So it was back to the old weaving shed where we had got the shafting from in the first place, and get scavenging some of their old hanging brackets. I had decided I was not going to be beaten by this minor piece of engineering. I managed to get three of them, so I put one in the middle, and with a new piece of shafting it all worked perfectly. That section is now about 40ft long and it runs round beautifully. The next job were to get another thirty odd foot of it going to where I wanted to build the engine house. I put two more trestles up made out of telegraph poles, with a bit more shafting but this is where I sort of came unstuck and nearly killed myself.

I had got it all up and tested it, but it had various wavers and tremors on it, and in actual fact things were not too good at all with this part. I put the problem down to one of the particular lengths of shafting myself, because the coupling, instead of being near a bearing, like it should be, were way out in the middle of the piece. This meant there was 9ft 6inches of space between the bearings and this big cast iron coupling in the middle.

It only needed to be a bit out of balance and it would start bending the shaft when it were revolving. So I decided we would shorten one piece of shafting and get a longer piece the other side so that we could get the coupling nearer to the bearing. I had got two planks from one trestle to the other one and was working up there. I was so mithered that morning as I had had a lot of visitors and ended up making a fatal mistake.

I had slackened off all the nuts and everything and instead of shoving, I pulled. The bloody thing came off at one end and went down and hit the plank with a 'bang', broke the plank in half and I went shooting up into the air. Now this particular piece of shafting were about 8ft odd long with a great big 8 inch diameter cast iron coupling on one end of it. So while I am flying through the air I am thinking to myself 'Where's that going to go?' When you are flying through the air in all directions it suddenly dawns on you that if that thing is going to follow you, one clout from that in the right place and you're dead!

I sort of shot off as far away that way as I could manage, if you can change directions in mid air (without wings) as you might say, and landed on the floor amongst all the old iron. It were a miracle I did not break my arm or my leg or something, even my neck. I'm sitting there on the ground still rather dazed by it all and still thinking, 'Where has that bloody piece of shafting gone?' because I had not seen anything of it since I took to the air and pulled at it.

Steam rollers, Victorian machines with ropes and chains hanging everywhere.

Fred on the footplate of his steam roller, throwing coal into the firebox.

What it had done was gone straight up in the air, across the yard and straight down through the top of the shed, and all that you could see were a short piece of it sticking up out of the roof. There was this great big hole in the top of my shed where it had gone through like a rocket, and hit a tin of yellow paint that had exploded all over the shed and all over my taps, dies and tools. In situations like this you look up and think to yourself, 'What am I doing all this for?' It would be a lot simpler with a little ten horsepower electric motor. I will never forget that anyway, a lesson was learnt that day.

I eventually overcame that problem with a longer piece of shafting. On the coupling I had there the nuts were down very deep countersinks. Now I had never had a socket set, all I had were open ended spanners and a few ring keys, so when I put this lot up I could not really get the nuts very tight, but it revolved beautifully.

In trying to get the whole setup right there were a lot of other trials and tribulations. Like I tried a 60ft length of hose pipe with two glass tubes stuck down the bend and two little hooks, hooked over the shaft to try to get it perfectly level. That did not seem to have much effect. Then I had a piece of piano wire from one end to the other with a big torque bolt at the end so you could play a tune on it. Then we had plumb bobs hanging from the shaft and that is really how we found out just how far out it were.

It is all right starting levelling from one end but by the

time you get to the other end you can be way out. This was as much as half an inch out in some places, not sideways, but vertically. You only need to be a bit out with one of them and once the revs get up it would all start shaking about. I had had one flying lesson, and wasn't keen to have a second. So I managed to get it running perfectly and in fact you could not see that it were going round, even when running at full revs. Nothing was shaking, nothing were vibrating. It were marvellous. When Christmas came round, my wife Alison bought me a brand new socket set, a box full of all these nice bright shiny silver sockets of all different sizes. On Christmas morning I wanted something to try these out on, so I went out into the garden and looked around, with the socket set in my hand. I remembered that coupling and so I tightened up the countersunk nuts. While I was out there I decided to spend the rest of the morning painting the piece of inserted shaft as it was beginning to turn rusty. This was painted bright red and it all looked very nice now, but the next time I got steam up it were all to buggery again.

The thing is these days they have all these tapered cones and things to tighten a shaft up on so that it is all perfectly circular and symmetrical. It is not just a case of a round hole that is a good fit on the shaft and you bang a key in. That has the effect of pulling it to one side and it has only got to be a few thou out and when you tighten the flanges it puts a set on the shaft about 1oft away. Then, when it is revolving one part starts fighting against another.

What they used to do in the old days was bang the key in and put the whole thing on a great big long lathe, get it running perfectly true and then take a shaving off the end of the flange. Then bolt it together. In the old mills all the shafting would be whistling round and it would look like chromium plate, you could not tell they were revolving other than the spokes in the wheels. All I could do out in the garden was to just slacken it off half a turn on each nut and it was all right again. The next thing was to get the stationary engine in position so that it were square with the shaft. I accomplished that with a lot of plumb bobs and by climbing right up to the top of a sycamore tree and having a piece of plastic down spout where the crank were going to be across the engine bed. All this performance were just to put the big stone down for the engine to stand on. I sighted it from the top of this tree, along the shaft to the plastic down spout. You can get things right by doing it the old ways. Then with lots of plumb bobs hanging down I could see that the flywheel would be vertical and not leaning over to one side. Everything was all put into position and the big 6in wide belt was put on while everyone around hoped and prayed we had got everything in the right place.

Here is an example of one of the signs collected by Fred.

Part of the line shafting at Fred's Yard.

Traction Engines
The Great Discovery
50 Year Time Capsule

Only £19.95
+ £3.50 UK P&P

2 FULL LENGTH DVD'S

LIMITED EDITION
COLLECTORS PORTFOLIO

Rare Documents & Photographs

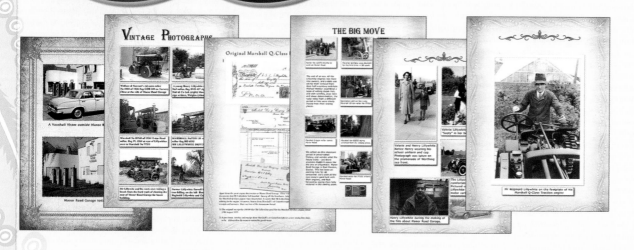

The Story of The Lillywhite Traction Engines

Steam Engineer, **Michael Webber** the day he unveiled the rare Marshall Q-Class Traction Engine in a secret building near Manor Road Garage, East Preston, Sussex.

There is a garage in East Preston, Sussex, that has kept a secret for nearly 50 years. Six traction engines, numerous vintage cars, and redundant plant, were stored at the Lillywhite Garage with only family and a handful of carefully selected people knowing what lay behind the closed doors.

So important and unique was the find that Heritage film maker Paul Donoghue was asked to scrupulously film the site and preserve the find on film for future generations.

DVD One Steam Traction Engines "The Great Discovery"

This film takes you into the Lillywhite Garage and shows the you the treasures that have laid undisturbed for almost half a century. Presented and narrated by respected steam engineer, Michael Webber, the story unfolds of how an Aladdin's cave of preservation exhibits have waited decades to be discovered.

The highpoint of the film is the unveiling of the extremely rare Marshall 6nhp Q-Class engine. No 73040. This engine was the favourite engine of the garage owner, Mr Reginald Lillywhite, and was stored in a special shed away from the garage.

Packed with rare footage, old photographs, lovely music and great interviews. (running time 60 minutes approx)

DVD Two Michael Webber`s Sussex Steam Rally

featuring the Lillywhite Engines. With two of the Lillywhite engines in steam, the other four engines presented as exhibits, cameras take you to the beautifully presented Sussex Steam Rally. Featuring interviews, working steam, arena events, miniatures, a fairground organ, model railway and many other great exhibits.

The highlight is seeing the rare Lillywhite Marshall Q-Class and the Wallace and Steevens Advance Road Roller `in steam` working after 50 years behind locked doors. (running time 60 minutes approx)

A page Limited Edition Document and Photograph also accompanies the two DVD`s in this presentation.

Reginald Lillywhite

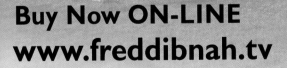

Buy Now ON-LINE
www.freddibnah.tv

Paul Donoghue Publishing
Office Suite No 7
Station Business Centre
Station Road
Clowne
S43 4RW
Telephone 01246 811112

PAUL DONOGHUE PUBLISHING

We accept all Major Credit Cards: Please make Cheques payable to Paul Donoghue

Some of the many old signs scattered around Fred Dibnah's yard.

It worked anyway, it goes round and the belt stays on the big wheel.

I have now got a new 3ft circular saw that I use to saw up the wood to feed the boiler. This makes the engine work, that turns the shaft and works the machinery, including the circular saw that cuts the wood.

The stationary engine itself was found in a mill at Chadderton, near Oldham but it were made in Bolton originally by Bennis Mechanical Stokers Ltd. This engine had driven five mechanical stokers on five Lancashire boilers. The mill was built in about 1904 and that engine were definitely installed right at the beginning and was not a later addition. So it were definitely there since the word 'go' and somehow or other it had survived the scrap man. Actually I know why and that were because it were so well hidden behind a door that you could open this door and walk right past it without seeing it. It were like set back in a cubby hole. I went to the mill to mend their chimney one time and that is when I discovered it.

I did a deal with the manager and brought it back home here. It were in a terrible state though.

The piston rod were all rusted steel, full of grooves and bumps. The valve rods were the same. The governors had been round that many times that they did not know whether they were coming or going. I had to find some new governors and make two new piston rings, a new piston rod and a new valve rod.

As luck would have it the bearings were all right. The gudgeon pin in the crosshead were an old bolt with a split pin through it. That must have come apart at one end because there was evidence that the small end of the connecting rod had been got red hot in a fire and hammered out rather crudely with a sledge hammer. It were all full of these big hammer marks and bangs where somebody had tried to straighten it out in the past. It had probably come adrift while the engine was running and the momentum of the flywheel had bent it on part of the framing of the engine.

The engine nameplate proudly boasts the name of Fred's first wife, Alison.

That was put in the lathe and a shaving taken off it to make it look brand new again.

I tried it first of all on compressed air, instead of steam just to see if it worked, and it did. The compressed air passing through it made it act like a refrigeration plant and the exhaust pipe went white with all these icicles sticking out from it. The vertical boiler was finally connected up and it has been working like that ever since. Not long ago I got a new boiler, a Danks 3-throw 1964 model, getting very modern now. This was in good order and is a lot better steam raiser than the vertical one. I also got a Wier pump so that the water could be pumped for the boiler. Who ever laid that up really looked after it because they greased it up and put a plug in where the exhaust pipe was so that no water could get inside.

The boiler came out of a mill at Oswaldtwistle (15 miles from here) when I knocked a chimney down one time. The boiler was like brand new and I did very well to get

it for the right price, not that many other people would actually want a boiler this big. But in a case like mine I really needed it. Well, I suppose I do not really needed it, but if you are going to persevere with this steam thing you might as well try to get it right.

There was nothing wrong with the old vertical boiler, other than it were made back in the days when coal was so cheap it did not matter how much you threw on it. When it were made, coal was probably only £2 for a whole wagon load and the owner could afford to buy say two loads a week to burn on it. Now a wagon load of coal costs hundreds of pounds. If you over stoke the boiler when it is driving the whole lot of what I have got it will start blowing off. You could easily drive a bigger engine with it, but the amount of fuel it takes is unbelievable. The big cotton mills back in the days of steam would burn something like 400 tons of coal in a week if they had a 3,000 horse power steam engine. Steam engines are very uneconomical things in some respects, so that is why they have faded out. Times have changed.

As Fred Dibnah became a national celebrity he often invited photographers down to the yard on Radcliffe Road so that they could use him as a study.

Chapter four

More Chimney Pieces

I arrived on a chimney job one Wednesday morning when it was really cold and frosty, Jack Frost nipping at your nose and all that. I had a wagon load of ironwork for the staging on top of the chimney and everything was absolutely freezing cold. The ironwork was all white and the parts were sticking to each other as you tried to prize them off the wagon. The little knick-knack (trade secret) here though was to put all the pieces on top of the manhole cover on the boiler and it got hot. When Donald (my assistant) tied it on the rope and sent it up, by the time it got to me it was still nice and warm and I did not need any gloves. It might be freezing cold but your digits were kept warm.

Soon after we had arrived we looked round the foot of the chimney and saw this ginger Tom cat 16ft up, sat on a packing piece behind the first ladder. I decided we

A telephoto view from the ground of Fred, perched 150ft upon the top of the chimney, December 1983. He vainly attempts to lure the ginger Tom from his lofty resting place into the RSPCA's cat box.

would unload the truck and get all the iron on to the boiler manhole cover, and with a bit of luck the cat might have decided to have come down by then.

When we finished what we were doing, it were still up there and it was now sat on the ladder, so I decided I would go up and have a go at getting it down. In retrospect I should have gone up the ladder three rungs at a time, then I could have caught it easily, because no way would it have risked falling off by trying to go faster than what I could have gone, as its legs were only short. But I didn't. I did not want to scare it, so I crept up the ladder rung by rung, and the bloody cat was keeping the same pace as me as I went higher and higher. When I was at the top of the first 16-pin ladder it was at the top of the second ladder, which were about 30ft up. I was beginning to think, 'I aint going to get this bloody cat. Problems'.

I was not over enthusiastic about going on this chimney anyway as it were so freezing cold. I came down and said to Donald,

"I'll go and have a word with works manager about ringing fire brigade and getting one of those teeny-bopper fire engines round."

We did not need one of them great big ones because it was only the height of an ordinary house. My idea at that time was for the fire engine to swing its ladder round, about 20ft above the cat and then I could go up underneath it. The fireman could then either knock the thing down or grab hold of it. I set off for the office and the manager said,

"Aye, if you ring fire brigade, the thing is they'll send us a bill. But if we ring the RSPCA they have an arrangement with the fire service and there is no bill involved."

So he rang through to his girl on the switchboard and told her the tale. He told her to ring up the RSPCA, tell them we have got this cat up our chimney and that we would like them to ring the fire brigade. While we waited, me and the manager had a chat about the great days of steam and all that, and how it would compare with modern machinery. We had a cup of tea, as you always do if there is any kind of crisis or disaster. By

The scene at the Bolton mill with both Fred and the cat at the top of the chimney.
Fred dangles the cat box, but again to no avail.

Doing his best to ignore his feline friend at the very top of the chimney. Fred makes a start on his real work by banging in the first pin for his staging. A few fret above him is the 2in wide ledge all round the chimney that the cat had previously occupied for much of its time up there.

Alison Dibnah is called upon to light one of the fires prior to a chimney demolition. Fred would never light them himself as he was superstitious.

A 1930s photograph showing many of chimneys that could be seen in the Bolton area.

which time I said I thought we had better go and have a look outside and see what the situation was. He got his overcoat on and as we went out into the mill yard it were like stepping out of a greenhouse into an icebox. The cold seemed to go straight through you.
Donald was standing there, looking up at the cat which was now about three quarters of the way up the chimney. There was another bloke there, with a black overcoat with three pipes up. I asked Donald,
"How's the thing got right up there?"
"This fellow here," he said, "he's an RSPCA man and when he got out of his van, looked up at it and said, 'ah, no problem I'll get it'."

Apparently he had produced this length of conduit piping with a piece of clothes line threaded up it. You need both hands for that so Donald had wondered how he was going to hook it, while climbing a vertical ladder. Anyway he had set off up the ladder with this thing in one hand and as he went up the cat went up further. When he got to about 50ft he had jibbed a bit and come down again, leaving the cat about a hundred odd foot up the chimney.

We were all stood there, all four of us looking up at it when the men from the fire brigade arrived.
"We haven't got a ladder long enough. Now you're going

to need a helicopter!" It were just a big laugh to him, sort of thing.
"Well we've got to have a go at getting it down somehow, haven't we?" I said,
"Can't just leave the poor thing up there."
As I went up again it went up even further still, until it reached a ledge about 6ft from the top, but this were only about 2in wide. There was not a lot you can do about it 6ft off the top of a chimney that's belching out smoke.

It was dinner time by now and the RSPCA man came back with a cat box full of cat meat. He said he would tie this to four bits of string, then I could sit on top of the chimney and dangle it down in front of the cat. He thought the ginger Tom would smell the cat meat and jump into the box after it. This man were like Einstein in reverse. Absolutely, clueless. The box were like a cage! You could see straight through it, the animal weren't going to jump off into space 160ft up, into a box that size. It would never go in there even if it were full of mice.
The cat was on this ledge, the RSPCA man had gone to dinner by this time and the firemen had gone back to fire station and it were one of the firemen who tipped off the local television people. When we got back from our dinner the ITV people were already there with their blue Range Rover and they said,

"What you going to do about that cat?" and all the usual interview type things.

"All I can do is go up there with this basket and do as I am told."

So I climbed back up the chimney yet again, and the smoke was coming out of it profusely and I had a crawl around. It was actually backing round on that 2in ledge, one wrong move and it would have been off. I felt like giving it a helpful kick by this time, but now the eyes and the ears of the world were upon me. No way would it come near me as I chased the bloody thing around the top of that chimney all afternoon – and the smoke were killing me.

Old photo of Fred's Land Rover parked in front of a chimney due for demolition.

High up, Fred Dibnah prepares for another day working in the clouds.

The famous Dart tower falls to earth after Fred has spent weeks propping the structure with telegraph poles.

Fred at the top of a chimney stack as he prepares the work area with scaffolding and planks.

Fred always used Land Rovers as his mode of transport when steeplejacking.

I came down at quarter to four, a beaten man. The thing was still sat there on that ledge over 150ft up then the RSPCA man came out with a classic,
"Tonight, when it gets hungry, it'll come down on its own."
If that was not wishful thinking, nothing is. Anyway, we all went home and it rained all night and it weren't too warm neither.

We arrived back there at 8.30 the next morning, to be greeted by every TV station and newspaper man in the land. A big crowd had gathered and everyone was very excited by it all.

"What you going to do this time Fred?" and "Are you going to have another go with the basket?"
All morning I chased it round the top of that chimney, this now being the second day. It just did not want to know. It were very bedraggled by this time and it had changed from being orange in colour to being nearly dark brown, with all the soot and the rain.
I came down and thought 'there's no way I'm going to get it'. No sooner had I got to the bottom of the ladder than the thing climbed right up onto the very top of the chimney. There, I could have caught it because I would be on an equal footing with it. It would not possibly think of jumping down from there, 6ft down the side of the chimney onto the 2in ledge.
Having got down again I was wanting to make a start on the real job in hand, so I decided to start putting the staging up which would be round and underneath the cat. It would then have a platform to come down onto

but in the meantime we would just ignore it and leave it up there, after all it had not minded being up there all this time anyway, plus I had decided that I didn't like the bloody thing.
We got half the scaffolding up and it would only have taken another two hours but it was dinner time so I started coming down the chimney. At that moment some fellow came rushing out of the crowd below and shouted out,
"We have the Animals in Distress people here." I was thinking, 'here we go'.
The mill manager overheard this fellow and got in a right flutter and shouted,
"We don't want any heroes here. Nobody up this chimney, bugger off, get out!"

The fellow moved off and I do not even know who he was, I only got a glimpse of him. He definitely was not the chap who eventually did climb up the chimney but probably some sort of spokesman for him.
Being dinner time we went home, the BBC men went to the Farmer's Arms and the ITV men went off somewhere to get some refreshment. One o'clock and we were on our way back. I have been looking at factory chimneys for the past 40 years, since I was a little toddler and I can tell a mile off when somebody is on top of one. It sticks out like a sore thumb. Even at three mile away you can see this little thing on the side. So I remarked to Donald,
"There's somebody up our bloody chimney."

LIGHTNING CONDUCTORS

SUPPLIED OR FIXED, ROPE OR TAPE.

Blackburn's Registered Holdfast and Encased Top Rod

Supersedes every Other kind.

COLLIERY CHIMNEYS

HOOPED, POINTED, RAISED OR STRAIGHTENED.

No Scaffold. No Stoppage of Works. Distance no object. .

ELECTRIC SIGNALS LIGHT

FITTED TO COLLIERIES, &c.

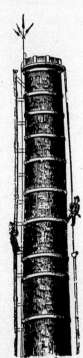

TELEPHONES to Speak from 500 yards to 5 miles. NO ROYALTY & NO CHARGE BEYOND FIRST COST.

Electric Bells, Batteries, Morse Keys, Insulators, Gutta-Percha and Lead-Covered Wire, all kinds Galvanised Signal Wire, and Electric Stores.

Estimates or Men Despatched on Receipt of Telegram.

Write for Illustrated Circular.

CHURCH SPIRES REPAIRED.

MAKERS OF

Weather Vanes & Terminals. Cast Iron Chimney Tops, Wrought Iron Belts, etc.

ESTABLISHED 1870.

JOSEPH BLACKBURN,

GRESHAM WORKS, 111, Waterway St., NOTTINGHAM.

Branch Offices:

London, Hanley, Birmingham, Plymouth, Cardiff, Dundee.

77

Rare poster from Fred's archive of steeplejack Joseph Blackburn from Nottingham.

Press photo of a smiling Fred Dibnah taken during a chimney demolition in his home town of Bolton.

"No there's not," Donald said. He can't see so well, I thought, but I insisted there was. When we got back to the site, it was total bedlam. There were black marias there, ambulances and the manager was there screaming away,

"Who is he up there? Where's he come from?"

The thing is this chap had actually managed to get hold of the cat and he had it in his hand. But he were stuck up there. The cat was in one hand and he was holding on to the ladder like grim death with the other.

"Somebody has got to get the fool down," I said looking around. So I climbed up the chimney to have a look at how he was fairing. He were only a young lad and I asked him,

"You all right then cock?" and he replied

"Yeah, I'm O.K."

The cat were giving him some stick though. It were no longer a friendly pussycat.

So I told him, in a calm voice.

"Look down between your legs and watch what I'm going to do. You'll be able to leave go with that other hand and change hands with the pussy." So he looked down and followed my actions of threading my legs through the ladder rungs and being supported just by your legs, and not with your arms. He could then get a better grip of the cat. I asked him if he thought he was able to come down and he hesitantly replied

"Yeah. I think so." So I told him what we do. I would go

down and untie the rope because it having been bit of an emergency over the past couple of days, I had not bothered with that, and it were all tied into every other ladder all the way down the chimney. I explained that when I got to the bottom I would tie this RSPCA man's cat box thing on and I would go back with it. I would open the lid, he would put the cat in, I would shut the lid and he would put the pin in through the shackles to keep it shut.

I climbed back up the chimney and he came down about two ladders from the top. The basket was on the end of the rope with Donald pulling it up. The lad put the pin that holds the lid shut, in the back pocket of his jeans and I opened the lid. He put the cat in, I shut the lid and he put the pin in, all as planned and we lowered it down.

The fumes out of a chimney make your nose run profusely and he turned round and looked at me, and there he was with these two candles of snot coming out of his nose and running right round his mouth and dripping off his chin. He could do nowt about it you see. He'd had too much of this smoke. It has that affect on you I can tell you.

I proceeded to come down and he followed me and we got down on to the floor. The television men were too busy with the ginger Tom to notice us and they had all these great big television cameras pointing at it and it looked far more frightened now than when it was prowling around on top of the chimney.

The police promptly grabbed the lad and carted him away and I never saw him again, though I don't think they charged him with anything. The RSPCA had the cat and not long after it had been brought back to earth they castrated the thing.

But the phone calls that Alison had over the two days that this were going on were unbelievable. It was actually on the television news the first dinner time of it being up there, and it went out on practically every news and current affairs programme throughout that week. More people saw that one episode than watched the whole of the TV series that we did.

Anyway, it seemed half the country was ringing up telling us how to get this cat off the chimney. There were some incredible suggestions like,

'What you need is a goldfish bowl with a mouse in it', and the best of the lot, 'You want a long plastic pipe and you knock the cat in the end of it with a stick and it'll come out at the bottom'.

Number one, where on earth were we going to get a 160ft length of plastic pipe the right diameter and two, when it comes out at the bottom it would be doing 90mph! How do they think them up?

The poor woman who it belonged to lived just over the mill wall, and the back gate of her house backed onto the mill yard. With all the commotion and the excitement she were frightened of coming out of the house and she never came near it. Then of course they had to advertise the cat in the Evening News, "Has anybody lost this cat?"

There were people as far away as Stockport saying it was theirs. It is back home now and believe it or not it used to come in the mill yard and sit on a pile of coal and watch us. That job had not really been started when all that happened so we were there for some time after that as we were reducing the height of the chimney. It never went near the chimney again though. It did not want to know about that.

Another chimney falls to the ground courtesy of Fred Dibnah.

Looking very sorry for itself after being sheeted by Fred. The traction engine
that was to become the most famous steam roller in the world.

The Laburnum Mill Saga

We got this job of knocking down this beautiful brick chimney at the Laburnum Mill, Atherton, the whole place was being demolished. Alison had this idea of running a raffle with all the proceeds going to Cancer Research. The person who held the winning ticket, which would be drawn on the morning, would help me light the fire at the bottom of the chimney, then retire to a safe distance. This is something people are always wanting to do and must be something to do with a destructive element in people's nature or something. It all went wonderfully well and we had already raised over £1,200 selling the tickets and there had been an enormous amount of local publicity for the event. There was even a chap coming up from Radio Severn Sound in Gloucester to record the whole event for radio. We had had several of our chimney fellings on television, but not on the wireless. This were new to me. It was the night before the Sunday morning we were due to bring the chimney down and we were just about to go up to bed.

Then the telephone rang and the woman on the other end says, "Somebody has set fire to your chimney stack." I immediately thought, 'this has got to be a hoax. It's quarter to one in the morning'. I thought 'definitely not on'. I asked her if she had a boss I could speak to, and as soon as she laid the receiver down I could hear typewriters and other telephone bells in the background. I realised that it was either a fire station or a cop shop. This other fellow comes on and he says, "It has been burning from about 12.30."
I asked him, "Is it still up do you know?"
"Yeah, just about. The fire brigade are there now. Can you get over there now?"
"I'm on my way", I said. It were about five miles from here and I drove at top speed as there was nothing on the road at that time in the morning. When I got there I could just about see that it were still up in the blackness, the fire being almost out. The fire engine was parked

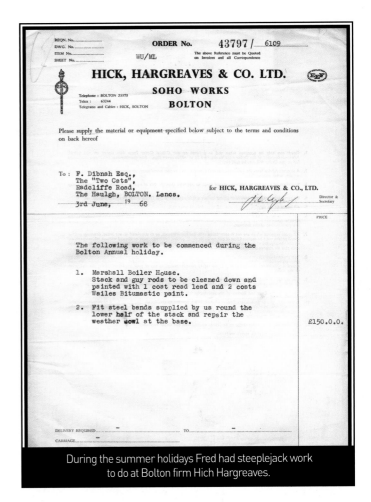

During the summer holidays Fred had steeplejack work to do at Bolton firm Hich Hargreaves.

outside the gate of the place, at least 200 yards from where the chimney was.
"Can't you get over there and put fire out?" I asked them.
"We're not going near it," they said, "there's a big bottle of propane stood right in the middle of the fire."
I was amazed at this and said, "That propane has been there since the fire was lit at 12.30. It's 1.15 in the morning now. If it ain't blown up yet, it ain't going to blow up."
By now it was quite black over by the chimney and there was not even any ware from the roadway. I borrowed a torch from a policeman and went over and had a quick look round it. When I got nearer the front I could see that of the 25 8in diameter props there were only three left on each side and they had suffered from the heat. This

bottle of propane were not pink any more, it were now a dirty grey colour. There was nothing issuing from the end of it and it were quite dead now.

It was evident that what the vandals had done was they had opened the top on the propane and let it blow out and thrown a lighted match into it. That is all the combustible stuff there was because during the course of the Saturday afternoon we had shifted all the small timber so that nobody would get the idea to light the fire. It was still up but then I wondered round the back and shone the torch on the horizontal crack. There was now no way we could keep it up. If it had been stable I could have stuck another prop under the middle and that would have saved it. It would have held it up until we wanted it to go, but it were too late. The crack was about 3/16inch broad at the back. When we had left it on Saturday afternoon it were only 1/64th of an inch and about 8ft round the circumference. Now it was practically half way round and at the worst part. 3/16th of an inch on a chimney that height means it is about 18in out of plumb and it was ready for going. Within another ten minutes it were creaking and groaning, so I advised the fire brigade, who had got brave enough by then to come near it, and the cops that had advanced cautiously down the road, that we had better all back up because it was going to go. We had only gone about 100 yards and 'whoof', down it went at quarter to two on the Sunday morning.

It were rather sad really because we caused a traffic jam on the Sunday morning and there was no chimney there. People had travelled from as far away as Sheffield to watch this chimney come down. They never got anybody who was responsible for it though, they reckoned they had their mits on some who had been split on. Even then they said,
"What can we charge them with if we do get them?" That whole place seemed to have a kind of jinx on it. At the other corner of the mill there was this great big brick tower, 170ft high. I had never done one of them before but we got it all ready for bringing down. Even during the preparations we had had a slight tremor.

The walls are very thin on these things for the weight they are holding up. We started cutting at this wall in the front, this being the way we wanted it to fall. I started at one end and another chap started at the other and we advanced along the wall towards each other. The wall was approximately 2ft thick and we had six or seven props each side of the cut as we progressed towards the centre. When we got to about a 2ft square in the middle this pillar of bricks began creaking and moaning and vertical cracks began appearing in it. Bits kept blowing off it and for three quarters of an hour we just stood there and watched this pillar go from 2ft square as though invisible beavers were going at it, down to a 4.5in square.

All the weight had been on this centre pillar with next to nothing on the props, but now the wedges had been squeezed to oblivion. There was now just this little piece left in the middle and I hit it with a hammer, 'boom' and it simply fell out. There were these two beautiful pyramids of crushed brick which had appeared before our eyes.

Our troubles were not over by any means. On the Sunday morning we lit the fire and there was a big crowd there as usual, including the people from German television who were making a film about us. A beautiful horizontal crack appeared across the back of the tower, marvellous, everything were in our favour, apart from the wind which were blowing in the wrong direction.

There were one very weak corner on the tower and one very strong one and the wind was blowing towards the weaker one. The fire was therefore being blown towards the corner so that meant the timber there would burn away first and the timber on the strong side would stay intact the longest.

It kept burning and it actually started to go, the whole lot of it, but then about 200 tons of masonry and bricks fell off the front. It then just sort of sat back on itself and it stood there, unmoved. There was this enormous hole in the front of it, it were terrible when you looked at it. The fire was still raging away underneath the brickwork that had fallen down. We had to get the fire brigade in to put the fire out. I then had to nibble out a bit more at the bottom, no more than another foot or so and it was away again and down it come. It was all very exciting and spectacular. We now know what to do if we get another one.

Another chimney is ready for the final drop.

Fred Dibnah's open plan boiler hous
Fred would burn almost anything to
his steam workshop running at full po

Chapter five
The German Connection

We had got used to the BBC people following us around sort of thing. They came with me to work, more or less moved in at home and even went on holiday with us when we went to Blackpool. But it came as something of a surprise when we had a letter from a German television company, A.R.D. saying that they wanted to do the same. They only wanted to do the one programme at that time so we took them to see the tower at Laburnum Mill coming down and they came with us to a traction engine rally. We got on with them quite well really and they sent us a copy of the film later and that did make us laugh. It was all in German of course, except that every now and again the commentary broke into a few English words – just the swear words – they seem to think I use occasionally.

We were only part of the final programme which were called 'Rund urn Big Ben'. From what we could make out it appeared to be about English eccentrics, so I don't quite know what we were doing on that.

They wanted me to go over to Berlin to film, but I wasn't sure about that – it would not be my first experience of that country. I started to tell that story before, in the previous MagBook 'Fred Dibnah The Early Days', so perhaps it is appropriate to recount that now.

When I was called up into the army I pleaded with them to give me an outside job, like building or engineering. But what I got was the cookhouse and when I heard that, I nearly deserted. I just could not imagine myself being a cook for two years. Fred Dibnah, Cook. It did not bear thinking about. Out of the 40 of us the army took on as cooks, there was not a single man who had previously had anything to do with cooking.

One fellow had worked a steam hammer in Sheffield. There were a lot of bricklayers from all round the place and a couple of joiners like myself. The nearest to the food business was a chap who had a knackers yard. But the army had made up its mind, and like it or not we were to be cooks and what better place to teach us than Catterick Camp.

Fred Dibnah explaining the finer points of steeplejacking to a bystander.

It were a dreadful place and our cooking lessons no better. I could not get away from the place fast enough, on my one weekend off. I practically walked from Catterick to Bolton which is a long way. As I neared home, I spotted some steeplejacks mending two big chimneys which were side by side. It meant a long detour on top of all my other walking, but it did my heart good to see them chimneys with red ladders up them. When you come to think about things it is a funny world. That weekend's leave were the low spot of my life. No sooner had I reached home at Bolton than I was on my way back to Catterick. I saw those two chimneys again with the steeplejacks repairing them and could have wept. Years later, when I were a real steeplejack myself, I brought both those chimneys down for BBC television. However, back to the army days. After finishing our cookery course came the great moment of volunteering for where you would like to go. I put my name down for Germany because some old soldier had told me things were more lax abroad. Anyway, I was loaded on a train, a boat and then another train. Eventually I ended up in a place like Belsen. It were a huge camp for tank regiments which someone said Adolf had built up for his many men.

Of course my place was in the wretched cookhouse. They told me to forget all about my training and concentrate on great dustbins full of spuds which were full of black eyes. So the potato-peeling section was where I spent most of my time. It were full of cockroaches, as was the canteen. They used to creep through the edges of doors and liked to rest in the curtains next to the dinner tables.

I have knocked around a bit myself but I found those army boys a rough lot. If there was a bit of barney and one did not like the other, he would flick a curtain as he passed the end of the table. This sprayed cockroaches not only into his enemy's dinner, but covered everyone else's food. You knew then that you had joined the professionals.

One slightly good thing about the cookhouse lark was that if you did breakfast and dinner, the rest of the day was your own. I did not mind starting at four in the morning because it gave me the afternoon to myself. I took to getting as far away from the camp as possible. The area was covered with big pine forests, Christmas tree jobs, where you could walk for hours and not see a soul. I used to tramp along thinking of my home and parents, Bolton and all them chimneys. Would I ever become a steeplejack and get red ladders up them? Would the name Fred Dibnah ever become as well known as my boyhood hero John Faulkner? These were dreary walks and thoughts.

The 14/20th Hussars as they were called, had only just arrived in Germany. They were supposed to be a cavalry regiment but had tanks instead of horses. However the officers were like sons of wealthy farmer types and they had arranged to bring their own horses with them.

Fred Dibnah and his fellow recruits outside the Army cookhouse.

Always the joker, Fred builds a chimney from tin cans.

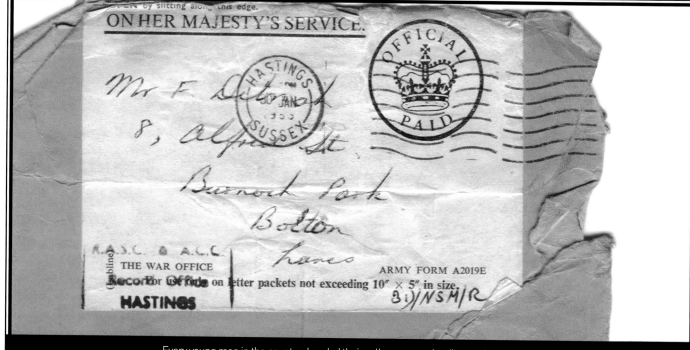

Every young man in the country dreaded their call-up papers landing on the doorstep.

One day I were proceeding along a forest track and came upon a barn with a big hole in its roof. In Germany all the roofs have a very steep pitch and gazing up at it was one of the officers from the tank regiment. Apart from his army boots he did not appear too smart. In fact he looked as if he were back home beside his hen pen. I bid him good-day sort of thing then he began talking about the steep roof and the difficulty of mending the hole.

When I told him that I were a joiner, a steeplejack and a lot more else he wanted to hear, there was delight all round. Soon we were joined by the major, who acted as God back at the camp. He were 6ft 6in tall and had a moustache almost a yard wide.

"Do you really mean," he said, enthusiastically, "you can mend that roof for us? You see our horses are on their way and we must have this barn to keep them dry and comfortable."

"Of course, sir," I assured him. "I can mend your roof if you can get me out of the cookhouse."

"Say no more," he said.

When I got back to camp, the monster who were in charge of the cookhouse were all smarmy like. He told me how pleased he was that I would be helping the major and other officers to house their horses. He had always thought me a good lad and all that.

I did the roof job as slowly as I could. When I was nearly finished the captain asked if I could lay bricks. You see, they now wanted stalls built for their horses. Well, I again assured him of my capabilities and in due course loads of bricks kept arriving. It suited me because the months were ticking by.

When I had finished the stalls, I spun out the job doing anything to please these horse mad officers. My masterpiece were a traditional British weathercock which I fitted to the top of that German roof. It were made of battered up army trays, spoons and things, all welded together.

There was nothing else I could make or fix around there and it looked as if I had to go back to the cookhouse when, low and behold, I seemed to have another stroke of luck. Twelve British fox hounds were arriving to join the horses, so they needed kennels and someone willing to look after them.

I have never been particularly close to animals and some of those hounds were ferocious. Heaven help the poor foxes who crossed their path. Worse still, the hounds were always hungry and even the local German butchers had problems supplying them with pigs feet and intestines, all in messy dustbins.

Instead of feeding men I became a dog cook, stuffing this offal and hard army biscuits into what they called a field boiler. That were bad enough, but afterwards came the dangerous job of going into the compound full of great big hounds. They seemed to think I were part of their feed and would even fight over me.

It were a bit of a problem for me, but one day I ran into this sort of hound expert. He said,

"You know what you want to do. You want to take a pitch fork in there with you, then lay the handle across the first hound that comes near you. If you hit him hard enough, he will see sense and so will the others."

So I did what the hound expert told me. The first beast got the handle across his backside, which made him turn on me all snot and teeth. I had to hold the pitch fork in front of me while thinking 'one false move and you're dead'. Meaning, myself of course. But the expert were right. That hound backed off and the others seemed to get the message. The next problem was when these officer farmers took their horses and hounds out hunting. Two or three dogs went astray each time. This meant yours truly had to go round the forest like a proper Charlie hooting on a hunting horn. We were sort of helped by the German gamekeepers. They used to return our dogs on the backs of motorbikes, after shooting them dead.

I did not worry too much about the number of hounds getting less. So was my time in the army. My two years National Service was nearly up when a Mr. Profumo had a brilliant solution for the lack of recruits. I had just one more fortnight to go when he announced that we National Servicemen would have to stay on for another six months.

There were about 40 National Servicemen in that particular camp and some of them had children they had never seen. You can imagine how they felt while I felt the same about my chimneys. After all we were only playing at being soldiers. No-one minded the real thing but this meant wasting more of our lives. There was a hard core of resentment about the camp and the army as a whole.

Little was printed in the local papers because the War Office acted very craftily. They invited the press to send over reporters who would ask National Servicemen their opinions on the extra six months. Of course it were all done in front of officers with NCOs right behind you breathing down your neck. Like all the other lads, I were as sick as a pig about it but I said,

"Well, if it's got to be done, we're good lads and we'll do it."

"Good lad," said the officers, while the NCOs seemed to breathe a little easier.

After this mockery of interviewing us, the reporters got a big booze up in the officers mess so that there was very little printed about how hard we were hit and suffered. No sooner had the reporters departed than the National Servicemen were dispersed all over Germany. Only two or three were put in each camp full of regulars and treated a bit like lepers.

I was sent to another camp about 20 miles away for the final six months and worked in its cookhouse. During my time off I could lie on a camp-bed thinking of what to do when I finally left the army. Should I return to being a joiner or should I have a real go at steeplejacking? I were 25 years old. I had done my bit for my country bit it had not done very much for me.

While I were lying there mithering my brain, I invented a lot of things that would improve steeplejacking. For example I thought up Dibnah's famous flying buckets, (which I described in my last book), whilst lying on that camp-bed in Germany.

So it looked as if I were going back to my first love, chimneys and steeplejacking. To tell the truth, there was never any doubt about it.

Fred Dibnah at the bottom of a chimney posing for the camera.

Fred Dibnah

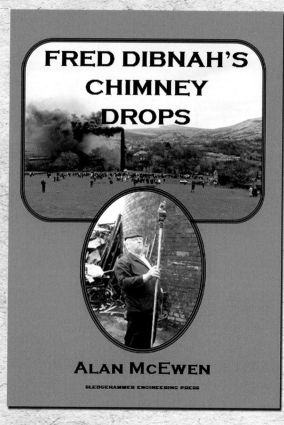

Author Alan McEwen, a retired Master Boilermaker and Steam Engineer well-known in the industrial heritage and steam world was a close friend of the late Master Steeplejac and Chimney Demolition Expert Fred Dibnah M.B.E. for close to 25 years, and within this beautifully produced book he has passionately and vividly chronicled 28 out of Fred's 90 amazing and often spine-tingling, dangerous chimney toppling exploits. Alan accompanied Fred on numerous extremely exciting and dangerous chimney demolition jobs all over North Western England, which enabled him to write the only authoritive account of Fred Dibnah's chimney toppling exploits.

This highly acclaimed book has received several brilliant reviews. This brilliant book chronicles 28 of Fred's amazing and often exceedingly dangerous chimney drops. Over 250 black and white and colour illustrations.

Great Value at only **£24.95** + £2.05 (U.K. Only)
Post and packing. Each Book
(please allow 14 (up to) days for delivery

IMMEDIATE
DESPATCH

BOTH BOOKS A4 SIZE HARD BACK QUALITY PUBLICATIONS
200 PAGES, WRITTEN BY WELL-KNOWN BOILERMAKER
ALAN McEWEN AND PUBLISHED BY
SLEDGEHAMMER ENGINEERING PRESS LIMITED
PUBLISHERS OF QUALITY BOOKS ON BRITISH INDUSTRIAL HISTORY

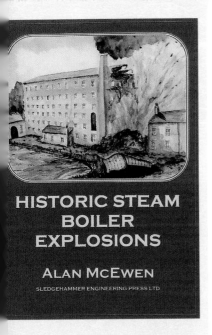

HISTORIC STEAM
BOILER
EXPLOSIONS

ALAN McEWEN

SLEDGEHAMMER ENGINEERING PRESS LTD

HISTORIC STEAM BOILER EXPLOSIONS

SLEDGEHAMMER ENGINEERING PRESS LIMITED
WORLD FROM ROUGH STONES HOUSE
FARLING TOP, COWLING, KEIGHLEY, WEST YORKSHIRE, BD22 0NW
TEL: 01535 637153 EMAIL: LANKYBOILERMAKER@BTCONNECT.COM
WWW.SLEDGEHAMMERENGINEERINGPRESS.CO.UK

£24.95

HISTORIC STEAM BOILER EXPLOSIONS

HISTORIC STEAM BOILER EXPLOSIONS includes basic histories of early industrial boilers such as: Balloon or Haystack, Waggon, Rastrick Vertical, Egg-Ended, Cornish, Lancashire, Scotch Marine Return-Tube; unfired pressure vessels called Kiers, as well as Locomotive Boilers and Marine Rectangular or Box Boilers.
The writing of this book - HISTORIC STEAM BOILER EXPLOSIONS - the first modern publication for decades that authoritively chronicles early British industrial boiler explosions, has been a long time coming for author, Alan McEwen, a qualified Boiler Engineer, now retired, for he has spent well over 30 years researching and gathering material, including many rare photographs, that has made the publication of this book a reality.

Within his book, Alan has chronicled 23 highly dramatic and informative stories based on his extensive research of the terrifying and devastating boiler explosions, including multiple explosions, that claimed the lives of hundreds of people whilst destroying the neighbouring buildings in Cotton Mills, Bleachworks, Collieries, Ironworks and other industries of the 19th and early 20th centuries. Included also, are 11 accounts of Traction Engine, Railway Locomotive and Marine Boiler explosions.

HISTORIC STEAM BOILER EXPLOSIONS is effectively two books in one.
Over 170 black and white illustrations.
£24.95 + Post and packing UK only £2.05 per book.
(please allow 14 (up to) days for delivery

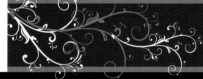

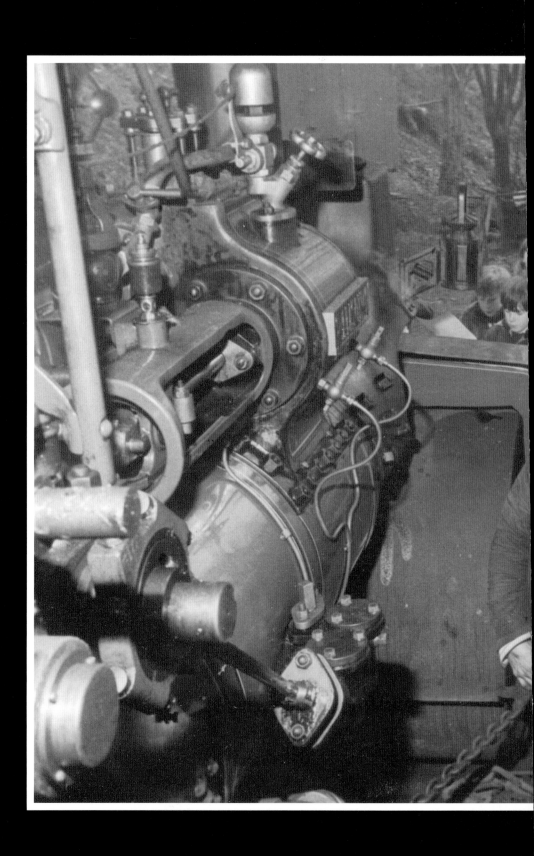

Following his appearance on national television, Fred Dibnah opens up his yard on Radcliffe Road to a group of local school children.

Chapter six
The Famous Fred

My chimney performances have attracted quite a following. Pensioners, children, strangers who describe themselves as chimney enthusiasts, and citizens who in former times might have attended public hangings. They all now turn up in the hope of seeing a disaster. I can assemble a crowd which would be envied by Bolton Wanderers. I play up to them a bit, act as if the damn thing is going to come down on top of them, or on a building. But no way is it going to do that. I have taken out half the bricks on one side and that is the way it is going to fall.

"Well done, Fred," they say when the dust settles. "Magic."

I have never had a disaster nor is there any reason why I should as it is all carefully worked out beforehand so that I know exactly where it is going to fall. But try telling that to the insurance companies. On one job I got paid £200 for bringing the chimney down. The insurance company got paid £700 in case I cocked it up. I had done all the hard work a week before and they never even set foot near the place.

One time I did not have two ha'pennies to rub together and nobody was interested in me. Then I risked life and limb. And still nobody cared. Then the television people showed what I did and now I get letters from all over the world.

The things people want to give me are incredible. One fellow offered me five lathes. Someone else wrote, "Dear Mr Dibhah, we are very concerned that your matches keep falling out of your pocket when you are on top of a chimney. Enclosed is a sample of our product, wind proof and weather proof matches".

I once had a 90-year-old lady come round to my place on a Sunday morning delivered by her son. She said her husband who had died was into steam engines.

Watching us on television with our steam engine had made her happy.

"It's the first she's smiled," said the son, "since father died." On another occasion we were out with the steam roller and we stopped outside this house and the lady came out and she was crying. She came up to me and said, "Oh you gave me a fright. I thought you were my Harry come back from the dead."

Apparently her late husband used to drive a green steam roller like ours and he used to park it outside the house where I had stopped, and at a distance I didn't look too unlike him. She invited me in for a cup of tea and showed me some photographs of him and a couple of little instruction books for steam roller drivers he had left her.

Unfortunately I did not have my glasses with me at the time so I said the next time I was passing I would call in and have a read of them. A few months later I was passing her door and she saw me and beckoned me in again. We had another cup of tea and she said I could keep the books as she knew I would be interested in them, but felt that when she passed on her family would not value them but just chuck them out. They do make fascinating reading so I have included a few extracts from one of them as follows:

Instructions to Steam Road Roller Drivers
The Lancashire Road Roller Co. Altrincham.
It is interesting to note that before Harry Hulse had the book the previous steam roller drivers to have used it had been a P. Abram, A. Moolley and a P. Johnson. In the back of the book was Harry's wages slip, well tattered and torn from 1933 and I am sure his widow will not mind if I quote this now as well.

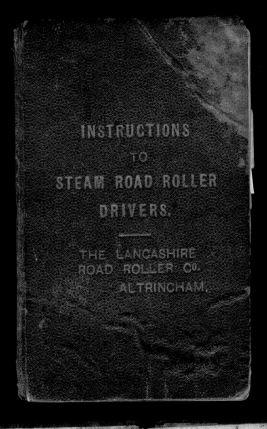

INSTRUCTIONS
TO
STEAM ROAD ROLLER
DRIVERS.

THE LANCASHIRE
ROAD ROLLER C0.
ALTRINCHAM.

PALATINE PRESS,
40/44, TONMAN STREET
MANCHESTER.

ROADSIDE WASTE LAND.

Steam Road Rollers, Vans, and Watercarts, must not be parked on Roadside Waste Land, unless permission to do so has been obtained from the local Surveyor.

Although this regulation applies in all parts of the Country, it is particularly enforced in Derbyshire.

Instructions to Steam Road Roller Drivers

No. 128

Driver

H. Hulse.

The following Instructions must be read, and remembered, by all drivers, as in every instance failure to comply with them renders either the driver or ourselves liable to a heavy fine.

The Lancashire Road Roller Co.

Altrincham.

This Book is the Property of THE LANCASHIRE ROAD ROLLER Co., and Drivers must RETURN IT when leaving their employ.

The Lancashire Road Roller Co., Altrincham .

3

The original book of instructions to Road Roller Drivers that was given to Fred by the widow of steam roller driver Harry Hulse.

TRAVELLING.

1.—FLAGMAN.

When a Roller is travelling or standing on any highway, a second man (or flagman) is required to be constantly with the roller.

If for any purpose the flagman leaves the roller, the driver must at once cease travelling and obtain assistance from the police. One person, however, must remain with the roller when on a highway, so long as the fire is alight, or whilst the roller has sufficient steam to move itself.

2.—WATER.

Rollers travelling through Manchester and Salford are allowed to take water from the Mains (for boiler purposes only).

Rollers travelling through Bury are not to take water from a Public Fountain, trough, well or receptacle for water, except with license of the Corporation.

The Lancashire Road Roller Co., Altrincham

4

WATER—*continued*.

In all other places permission must first be obtained before taking water from mains, ponds, streams, reservoirs, etc., from the owners, except from recognised watering places.

If a driver finds his roller urgently requiring water, application should be made to any policeman for assistance.

3.—SMOKE.

It is an offence punishable by a fine of £5 for a Steam Roller passing through a town or village to make smoke.

As far as possible, when travelling through populous districts, coke should be used. Otherwise, the roller must be fired outside the towns or villages so as to avoid making smoke during the passage through.

The Lancashire Road Roller Co., Altrincham

5

4.—REGISTRATION NUMBER PLATES.

Every Steam Road Roller is now compelled by law to carry two registration Number Plates—one at the front and one at the back of the roller—in such a position, and kept clean and uncovered so that they are easily visible, and can be easily read by the police.

When hauling a water cart, sleeping van, or any other vehicle, the last vehicle must show on the rear a Registration Plate, bearing the same number as that on the engine.

The penalty on the driver for not having the Registration Plates on the roller or trailing vehicle, or for having them covered or obscured, is £20 for the first offence, and £50 for each subsequent offence.

A Steam Roller is also required to carry the Paper License as carried by motor cars and traction engines, and this must be fixed to the side plate of the engine, next to the Name Plate, and kept clean.

The Lancashire Road Roller Co., Altrincham

6

5.—NAME AND WEIGHT PLATES.

The Roller must have fixed to it in a conspicuous position :

    (a) The Name-plate giving our name and address.

    (b) A Plate giving the nominal weight of the engine.

The Van and Water-Cart must each have fixed to it in a conspicuous position :

    A Plate giving with weight of the vehicle.

6.—OBSTRUCTION.

It is an offence to purposely obstruct the passage of any highway, and drivers must give as much space as possible to other traffic.

Special attention is drawn to page 18 giving times a roller may stand, and also about passing through narrow streets.

7.—SPEED.

The speed of a roller must not exceed four miles per hour in the country, and two miles per hour in cities, towns, and villages.

The Lancashire Road Roller Co., Altrincham

7

Steam roller drivers were given strict orders about their conduct when constructing roads. They also had to abide by the rules laid out in the instructions to the Road Roller Drivers handbook.

WATER.

Rollers travelling through the Heywood and Middleton Districts are allowed to take Water from the Mains for Boiler purposes only from the Heywood & Middleton Water Board Hydrants.

WATER.

HEYWOOD & MIDDLETON WATER BOARD.

The supply may be obtained from the Sluice Valve Hydrants near to the undermentioned places which have been fixed specially for that purpose. Sign plates have been fixed opposite the Sluice Valve Hydrants to indicate the position. Water must not on any account be taken from any other Hydrants or from any Dwelling Houses, Watering Troughs, &c., and any person infringing this regulation will be liable to prosecution.

HEYWOOD DISTRICT :—

Opposite Ryecoft House, Rochdale Road East.
Opposite Hopwood Liberal Club, Manchester Road.
Between Summit Inn and Boohole Farm, Bury New Road.

MIDDLETON DISTRICT :—

Water Tank, near Public Fountain, at junction of Manchester Old Road and Manchester New Road.
Junction of Rochdale Road and Hollin Lane.
Adjoining Three Arrows Inn, Heaton Park.

NORDEN DISTRICT :—

Adjoining Grimes Farm, Edenfield Road.

17.—LOCO'S STATIONARY ON HIGHWAYS.

A Steam Roller must not stand in the following Boroughs for more than the stated times.

Barrow-in-Furness Boro'	30 mins	Lancs. C.C.	30 mins.
Bootle Boro'	30 ,,	Staffs. C.C.	30 ,,
Burnley Boro'	30 ,,	St. Helens Boro'	30 ,,
Chester City	30 ,,	Smethwick Boro'	30 ,,
Cheshire C.C.	30 ,,	Walsall Boro'	30 ,,
Crewe Boro'	30 ,,	Warrington Boro'	30 ,,
Derby C.C.	30 ,,	Wednesbury Boro'	30 ,,
Derby Boro'	30 ,,	West Bromwich Boro'	30 ,,
Hyde Boro'	20 ,,	Wolverhampton Boro'	30 ,,
		Liverpool Boro'	30 ,,

18.—NARROW ROADS.

Where for a continuous length exceeding one hundred yards, a highway comprises a carriageway or cartway of a width less than 16-ft., a person in charge of a loco. shall not drive or suffer the loco. to be driven upon the carriageway or cartway unless a person accompanying the loco. shall precede the loco. for a distance reasonably sufficient to warn the drivers of vehicles of the approach of the loco.

18

QUESTIONS BY STRANGERS.

On no account must drivers discuss with strangers particulars of their work, where they are travelling to, or where they have been working, or any information concerning their present, past, or future work. Firms competing with us have endeavoured to obtain such information to take our work from us, and we expect our drivers to assist us in every way they can to retain this work.

This Road Roller Drivers handbook was one of Fred Dibnah's prized possessions. He would often get it out and show visitors the rules for steam men back in the 1930-40s.

As Fred Dibnah's fame grew he was offered the chance to do personal appearances.

Since the television series was shown, in addition to being given things we also get asked to appear as what they call the 'guests of honour' and to officially open things. At one time this was just a local things like a Dr. Barnardo's shop but now it can be all over the country. I get invited to lots of traction engine rallies and if I went to all those I would never get anything else done so I often have to refuse.

Even those I do go to are often too far away to take my own engine as I do not agree with the idea of sticking it on the back of a lorry. If I cannot drive the roller all the way there under its own steam then it has to stay at home.

Once they invited us down to Cornwall so I went with Alison and the three girls to the West of England Steam Society's Rally at Silverwell Farm near St. Agnes, and we officially opened that.

Then it was the Holton Working Steam Rally near Oxford. While we were there for the weekend they loaned us a very rare Richard Hornsby engine 'Maggie' which dates back to 1886.

People are often requesting us to visit them and then they say, "Don't forget to bring your steam roller with you Fred."

These people do not realise what is involved in firing up a 12-ton steam roller and driving it out on the street and then putting it back in the shed again and cleaning it all out again. They seem to think it is like turning a car ignition on. We have even had a request from a bookshop where we were going for a signing session to take the roller along. I thought we would have to sell a lot of books just to pay for the coal so we went in the Land Rover instead. When we got there the shop was in a pedestrian precinct and we could not even park that anywhere nearby.

Other people turn up and knock on the door and expect you to get the engine out of the shed so that they can take a photograph of a relative standing by it. Then the other day some more television people came on the phone and said that they wanted the engine in steam standing outside the shed so that they could film a few details of it. I said, right that will cost you so much. "We can't afford that!" they said and offered me about half. Eventually we agreed on a figure and they came

round. When they arrived there was about six posh limousines and each chap wore a fancy suit and had a dolly bird assistant with him. Each of them were fancily dressed in pink silk overalls. All in all they did not give the impression of being too hard up.

I got the engine out of the shed for them and they started filming various parts of it for some technical programme something educational anyway. Then one of them shouts across, "Hey Fred. Can you come over and tell us what this bit does?"

So I went over and started explaining and the cameras kept rolling. Next thing, we saw Alison rushing out from the house and she says to them all, "We agreed a price to film the engine. Now you are interviewing Fred for television. That's an extra £25." We got it too!

Fred Dibnah enjoying his new found role as a celebrity.

Fred breaks through the mock wall and enters the telephone exchange car park.

Job done, as the press, radio and television media get their story.

British Telecom General Manager Andrew Hurley enjoys a photo call with the famous steeplejack.

I get asked to go to some unusual places but one of the more interesting ones was to open a new telephone exchange for British Telecom at Swindon. The general manager of the telephone area happens to be a steam enthusiast himself and his son regularly drives a friend's traction engine. They arranged all the transport and everything and I arrived in Swindon where a beautiful Burrell traction engine were sat there waiting for me. It were a beautiful day and we chuffed all round the town with a little trailer on the back which carried a board reading, 'From the Steam Age to the Electronic Age with Fred Dibnah'. This trailer carried extra fuel,

and also some people from a local radio station who broadcast everything we said.

We had a fine old time clattering and whistling round this town, once so famous for building steam locomotives for the Great Western Railway. But then the crunch came. We arrived at the exchange, and the yard they wanted me to park the engine in only had a narrow gateway. No way would I get it in there, as there was a brick wall right across the end of it. As we came round the corner and approached it I asked, "What do you want me to do now?"

It makes you wonder if BT would go for the flat cap,
fag in hand image today?

The workers at the telephone exchange make sure that they get their photos taken with Fred Dibnah.

"Just keep going Fred," they said. "This engine should get through there without too much trouble, open her up". 'They know what they're doing', I thought, so with a blast on the whistle we opened the regulator and went straight at the wall, 'crash'! We were right through it with bricks flying in all directions and a cheer from the people that had gathered round.

The steam engine BT hired for the day that Fred Dibnah came to town.

Does anyone remember Long Life beer?

Lovely photograph of Fred driving the traction engine around the town.

I was a bit disappointed really when I realised the wall was a dummy made of polystyrene bricks, but it was very convincing. I then had to make a speech before cutting the tape which formally opened the premises. This was about three floors up, on the outside, so I was whisked up in a hydraulic platform. Then we had a wander around inside and saw all the electronic wizardry. It was all a very far cry from the Victorian mills of my home town of Bolton.

I also get asked to appear on various television programmes these days including an early morning talk on TV AM and we had the girls on 'Whose Baby?' a few months back. Then another time I was the judge on 'The Great Egg Race', as the three teams were asked to make

a steam engine from the various bits and bobs they were given. They asked me first of all how I would do it. I looked around the things and had to admit it were rather difficult. How do you make a steam engine when lots of the parts are plastic? Anyway, about six hours later the teams had concocted various devices which were powered by compressed air rather than steam. In the meantime they got me to explain how a real steam engine worked by using an Isle of Man loco that had had one side cut off.

My most surprising television appearance though was not me in person at all. It was Mike Yarwood impersonating me on his Christmas show. Now you can't get much more famous than that can you?

Early photograph of Fred Dibn...
yard which in his words was a pro...
of "Blood, Sweat and Bloody ...

Chapter seven

The Rise and Fall of King Steam

People often ask me why it is that there were so many chimneys in this part of the country and why it is I am now bringing them down. To understand this you need to know something about the history of the weaving and spinning industry in Britain.

Humanity in general has been weaving and spinning material for centuries, but for a long time using very crude methods. For some unknown reason Samuel Crompton, Richard Arkwright and other chaps like them with inventive type brains, all lived in the area. Crompton who lived in Bolton, invented the spinning mule in 1780. The business men of the time started constructing these things and of course began to make the money. It was such a fine piece of tackle that these businessmen soon realised that if you had say 20 of these inside a shed, and a lot of little lads working them, you could make yourself a fortune. The other aspect was that

The Earl of Bradford's family crest which can be still be seen today on Fred's house on Radcliffe Road, Bolton.

there were plenty of coal about nearby which were an advantage, because in them days transport were a bit awkward. That is basically how the cotton era started.

It all grew and grew and developed; steam engine builders, boiler making companies all got bigger and bigger. About a hundred years ago the mills in Lancashire employed about half a million people, producing something like 10,000 tons of cotton every week. By the 1900s the spinning mills were at their finest. Most average mills had four boilers and a 2-3,000HP steam engine that turned it all round. Some concerns were even bigger and they had three or four mills with two or three engines and two boiler houses and two great big chimneys.

A lot of the owners were so far seeing that they would purchase the field next to their site with the idea of extending and building another mill. Many of the mills owned a huge amount of land but now it is all being sold off for housing estates and what have you.

They seemed to have this idea at the time that they were going to last forever. You only need to look at the architecture of the buildings to see that. Some people refer to them as the dark satanic mills, but you want to look at some of the rubbish they are building today! They have recently cleaned up some of the mills and they really are beautiful, with all their fancy twiddly bits. Some of the mills were completely self contained and they even had their own bore holes for water, their own blacksmith's shop, joiner's shop and mechanic's shop. The only thing that they bought from outside was the coal. By the 1920s many of the engineers began to realise that the great age of steam was nearly finished and the electric motor started to take over fast.

Going back to when I was about 14 years old, as well as steam engine builders round here there were spinning and weaving machinery builders that were not too far away Mather & Platt, Dobson & Barlow and lots of others and they were world beaters in their field. Their backroom boys were still improving and making better machinery. By then the mills that were still privately owned were now in the hands of the third generation of owners. These people were born into apathy with silver ware on the table in great big mansions. They took it in turn all round

The steam roller in the line up as Fred and his family enjoy a weekend away at a Lancashire Traction Engine Rally.

the town to be mayor and all that sort of thing. One half of the family built steam engines and boilers while the other half owned the spinning mills, so they did not want to modernise the places. One family owned about seven mills (I've had my ladders up many of them) and that was probably the biggest complex in Europe. Originally they had seven steam engines but eventually they scrapped these little ones and got in bigger ones that would power a couple of mills. They knocked all the little chimneys down and built two great big ones.

I have got one of the iron plates off one of their engines built in 1888, 'John Musgrave & Sons, Ltd, Engineers Bolton'. That engine worked right up to 1960 driving a big mill. They simply never modernised. Dobson's kept building the machinery that would keep them in the forefront of the world, but the mills did not want to buy it. They still had their own ancient mules rattling up and down on knotty pine floorboards.

The first black men I ever saw were the sons of rich merchants from afar, and they were all at the technical college across the road. There they were learning all about the cotton trade and the machinery. Then they went back home, daddy bought them Dobson's latest machinery and got them going. Eventually they thought their machinery was getting out of date so they went and bought Swiss and German machines which were improvements on the others.

Now to compete with the foreign competition Courtaulds have had to buy new machinery. Mather & Platt have gone, Dobson's have gone so they have had to go and buy the Swiss and German machines. Nearly every working mill has foreign machinery in them, apart from the carding engines. Some of these still have 'Mather & Platt 1915' on the castings on the ends but they are totally different inside to what they were in 1915. They have got new guts inside the old frames where the mills have had a go at modernising themselves.

Now this foreign machinery in the mills that are left is working day and night and never stops. There is only about 12% of the people that were working there originally, and they are more like robot places.

Tel. 061-794 4711
BT GOLD END028
Fax No. 061-794-6497
Telex: 669806 (SALCIT)

When calling please
ask for MR.D.R.TINKER
on Direct Line 061-793 -2009

CITY OF
SALFORD

THE NEW ERA

Environmental and Consumer
Services Manager,
M.L. Jassi, B.Sc.(Hons), D.M.S.,
M.I.E.H., M.B.I.M., F.R.S.H.

Crompton House, 100 Chorley Road,
Swinton, Salford, M27 2BE.

Environmental and Consumer Services Department

My ref: PNW/DRT/MT
Your ref:
Date: 9th August 1991

**DEMOLITION SITE, MONTONFIELDS MILL,MONTONFIELDS ROAD
ECCLES
CLEAN AIR ACT 1968 - SECTION 1**

Dear Sir,

I write further to my visit to the above mentioned
site, on Sunday 4th August 1991, immediately following
demolition of the industrial chimney, and subsequent
to complaints of an extensive black smoke emission.

I was informed that the emission was due to the burning
of tyres around the bottom of the stack to kindle the
supporting props.

As I made clear, on the day, such action is contrary
to Section 1 Clean Air Act 1968, and both the occupier
of the site, for the purpose of the demolition, and any
person who causes or permits the emission, shall be
guilty of an offence.

In this particular instance, I do not intend to report
the matter for the consideration of legal proceedings.

However I know that you are fully aware of the legal
position regarding burning on demolition sites, and
I must advise that any further demolitions of this
type, or blatant disregard of the provisions of Clean
Air legislation, within this City, will result in the
institution of legal proceedings.

An identical letter has been sent to Reddish Demolition
and a copy has been sent to Elite Homes.

I would appreciate any comment you may wish to make.

Yours faithfully,

D.R.Tinker

Principal Environmental Health Officer(Pollution Control)
Fred Dibnah, Steeplejack,
Park Cottage,
121, Radcliffe Road,
BOLTON, BL2 1NU

This letter from the City of Salford Environmental Department made
Fred Dibnah very angry. Fred took it very personally that they
questioned his chimney-felling method.

Great example of Fred's work as this chimney awaits demolition.

It makes you wonder how the chimneys managed to stand upright after all the brickwork had be removed by Fred Dibnah from the bottom?

One mill after another shut. There was once about 200 in Bolton, now you can count them on one hand. There is one privately owned, or at least owned by a limited company and still trading under its own name, but the other three are all owned by the giant Courtaulds. Tootals, famous for their shirts and ties once had a whole empire here, with about five chimneys on.

I remember Princess Anne coming on one occasion and saying something like, "They've modernised now. The future is all bright and rosy." That place is flat now, it's a cinder patch. Once they said 'England's bread hangs on Lancashire's thread'. There was more money made in these parts than any other part of England except perhaps the steel towns like Sheffield. But as for the concentration of boilers and chimneys there could not have been any place in the world that had more. You need to think of the sheer power in horsepower contained within the town at the height of the milling industry. There were dozens of 3,000 horsepower engines. Some of the buildings are still there but with something like a washing machine motor in them. They were very proud of their engine rooms and they were kept spotlessly clean. The door was always at the top of a flight of steps and it was always very well joinered. It was more like cabinet made than joinered and they always had brass key hole plates and knobs on. I now have a pair of these brass door knobs on the door of our living wagon.

No one was allowed into the engine room, it was taboo. Even the manager of the works himself was scared of going into that forbidden place as the bloke who ran the engine were like a little god. Those engines were really magnificent machines, even if in reality they were very uneconomical.

The last two steam engines in Bolton must have been among the very last of the real big ones to actually be used commercially. They were at Warmsleys Forge and these two were 30ft tall, vertical single-cylinder rolling mill engines and ran right up until April 1983. When the firm started in the 1860s they had two steam hammers and three rolling mill engines. When the first of these were removed it was not scrapped but went to the Ironbridge Gorge Museum in Shropshire complete with one of the steam hammers. That well-known museum has acquired a lot of its tackle from the Bolton area. There are quite a lot of stationary steam engines preserved in museums, but to me these are merely mounted and stuffed, they are not what I call working any more. Some of them have their 'steam days' when they light the fire and they make the flywheel go round, and even if they have a few ropes on they are only running a pulley up in the rope race. The engine only goes 'chuff, chuff' as there is no shafting upstairs for it to really get to grips with.

When the engines worked at full pitch they had a 100 tons of weight on them and you could feel the vibrations, very different to when it is out to graze. It is the same

A steeplejack's dream. Working in the sunshine.

the same with traction engines at a rally. You see these engines when they have knocked out a cog and they are just ticking over. People say, 'Beautifully smooth'. You connect the weight up and then listen to the row it makes, especially when they are knackered.

However, I have my own little stationary engine here in the garden and that really does do some work. It is not just a show piece. It may only have 90 odd foot of shafting to turn but at least you can tell that it's having to try to do it. You can put your hand on the shed and you get some idea of the effort that is involved to turn that all round. Where as if you knock the belt off it runs as sweet as a nut.

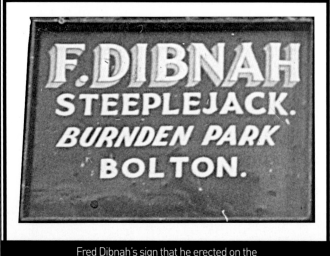

Fred Dibnah's sign that he erected on the site of all his early steeplejack jobs.

Queen Street Mill

The use of steam in the weaving industry finally came to an end in March 1982 when Queen St Mill at Harle Syke, near Burnley, was closed. This was the last working steam-powered textile mill in Britain and had remained virtually unchanged since it was built in 1894. Its closure was no surprise in the hard-hit textile trade but its claim to fame as the last steam-powered textile mill ensured it received national news coverage.

A major element of Britain's unrivalled industrial heritage appeared to be in danger of being lost for ever. It is situated in the Harle Syke conservation area and is bordered by countryside and the unique qualities and character of the mill have attracted attention from both this country and overseas. Burnley Borough Council and Pennine Heritage Ltd have been working together to produce a scheme to save the buildings and contents with work now underway to open Queen St Mill as a major tourist attraction. It was soon realised that it was essential for it to be retained as a working mill and not as a static museum piece.

Traditional products will be woven on the original Lancashire steam-powered looms so the original 500 horsepower steam engine will once again be in operation.

The chimney at Queen Street Mill in Burnley, Lancashire.

The 500HP steam engine that powered over 300 weaving looms.

Among the items I have come by over the years is a large ledger type book that has gold leaf letters on the front reading 'Heron Mills Ltd, Engine Statistics'. It is an amazing book for these days as it records every conceivable fact about the engines at the mill, entered every week by the engineman. Written in copperplate writing the statistics appear in columns. The first entry, which is typical of every subsequent week for many years reads:

1908

May 13th

Coal Stock last week: 35 tons Revolutions: 276,419

Coal Received: 62-15-2 Hours + Mins: 57.35

Coal in Stock: 35 tons Cyl. Oil used Galls.: 13

Coal consumed: 63 tons Shafting Oil used Galls.: 5

I.H P. HP Cyl.: 737 Average temperature of

I H.P * LP Cyl: 644 water at econOmiSer inlet: 112

I H P Total: 1381 Average temperature of

Lbs of Coal per I H P.: 1.77 water at economiSer outlet: 280

General Remarks:

*Input Horse Power High Pressure

Low Pressure

The General Remarks were entered as appropriate

usually referring to any

faults, repairs and maintenance but some of these are:

17/6/08 Short time (The revolutions was down to 148,412 for the week).

30/10/12 New assistant started this morning.

7/11/12 New assistant got hit with crank. (Off work.)

21/11/12 Put fireman in Engine House and got a fresh fireman.

4/1 2/12 Very cold week and change of fireman.

30/4/13 Packers strike.

4/6/13 Packers strike settled May 31 / 13

16/7/13 Stopped Saturday for King & Queen visit to Oldham.

8/4/14 Yorkshire miners strike.

29/3/22 Mill stopped for engine repairs.

The last week of fully detailed entries was 29/5/28 then just half a doen brief notes on some repairs in 1929 with nothing at all until 8/9/45. The columns of statistics were never resumed but notes were written in, across the printed columns describing any fault and repair, boiler washouts etc. This carries on like this until the last entry which is dated 26/6/62: "Got steam up at 5.55 engine started at 6 00. 6.30 pump broke but soon fixed. Engine still kept going. Stopped at 6.45".

Fred's two traction engines in his workshop.

Fred heads back to the house for a dinner break.

Fred Dibnah always enjoyed the glory of being England's most prolific and famous steeplejack. But behind the scenes he had to endure many hours of hard graft.

As an infant Fred was always fascinated by steeplejacks.
As an adult he became the most famous steeplejack in the country.

Fred gave out 1000s of these business cards. They didn't bring in much
work as the cards became a collector's item for Fred Dibnah fans.

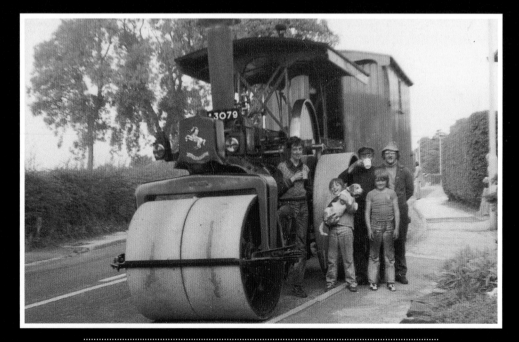

Fred enjoying a cup of tea by the side of the road.

Auto Express
THE CAR NEWS WEEKLY

GET 6 ISSUES OF AUTO EXPRESS FOR £1

Auto Express is THE car news weekly, delivering the big motoring news stories, scoop pictures, first drives of new cars and exclusive road tests EVERY WEEK.

Nothing moves in the world of cars without Auto Express knowing about it, from future models to changes in the law. Plus, our weekly guide to used cars will keep you fully updated on what's happening in the market.

This special offer of **6 issues for £1** means you pay less than 20p per issue. Continue reading and you'll **SAVE 42% on the shop price**.

EVERY ISSUE IS PACKED WITH:

▸ Britain's **biggest car news section** – with pages of all the latest new models and motoring stories from around the globe

▸ The **first and fastest new car drives** and road tests with all the verdicts, facts and figures you need to know

▸ World **exclusive spy pictures of pre-launched cars**, so you know what's in the pipeline and can plan your purchase accordingly

CALL NOW 0844 844 0026

Or order online at: **www.dennismags.co.uk/autoexpress** using offer code G1004DIB

THE GAFFER

F. DIBNAH Steeplejack BOLTON

LONG VEHICLE

For Sale
Wright
Manley
Estate Agents
Whitchurch
01948 662281

079

FOR SALE

POLICE, fire brigade and ambulances raced to the Deane Road mill of the Croal Spinning Co. after a body was seen hanging from scaffolding at the top of the mills' 210ft chimney — but it turned out to be a dummy someone had put there for a joke.

F. DIBNAH Steeplejack

Fred Dibnal

SCRAPBOOK

Felled (1937)

ANOTHER of Oldham's landmarks disappeared on Tuesday night when the Pearl Mill chimney, Abbeyhills, was felled.

The task of bringing down the silent sentinel, which has stood there over 40 years and marked the spot of a once-active mill, proved a bigger thing than the demolishers expected.

The work was undertaken by Messrs. Cartledge and Shackleton, steeplejacks of Chapel Street East, Ardwick, Manchester, and the chimney, which was the biggest in the town, being 255 feet high, had a base of 64 feet in circumference.

The demolishers began their task on Sunday, but it was impossible to complete the job that day, and on Monday the work was delayed by a large fall of soot on to one or two of the men.

It had been hoped to finish the work on Tuesday afternoon but the drop was again delayed through the strength of the stack. The chimney was in such a weakened condition that it could not be left and work proceeded in the dark.

It was around 8 40 p.m. when the chimney gave way, broke in three places, and collapsed on the portion of the mill site where it had been expected to drop. About 200 people saw its end.

St. James' Church

Telephone:
BOLTON 31303

Established
1958

REPAIRER OF
CHIMNEYS, CHURCH SPIRES, LIGHTNING CONDUCTORS
ERECTED FLAG POLES PAINTED AND REPAIRED : CHIMNEYS FELLED OR
DEMOLISHED : CHIMNEYS BANDED AND POINTED : IRON CHIMNEYS PAINTED
AND REPAIRED : WEATHER VANES MADE AND FITTED

F. DIBNAH

STEEPLEJACK

PARK COTTAGE, RADCLIFFE ROAD
BOLTON BL2 1NU

FULLY INSURED

Ocean Mills, Edbro

M..

....

2nd Januarys 1983.   p.

The British Broadcasting Corporation,
New Broadcasting House,
P.O. Box 27,
Oxford Road,
Manchester, M60 1SJ.

Dear Sir,

    After 5 years of film making with the BBC. I have come to
the conclusion that repairing factory chimneys, pays better wages
than the BBC. do, and so therefore, I do not wish to carry on making
films.

    All the upheaval and expence on my part out weighs the
rewards gained, it has become virtually impossible to do any work
in my work shop in the garden, because of a constant stream of
visitors with cameras.

    Before all this I lead a peaceful and tranquil life and
now have the VAT man banging on the door looking for money I haven't
Had even the Income Tax man says I am better off repairing factory
chimneys.

    I do not wish to become a millionaire but a bit of fair
play would have been appreciated.

    I signed a contract for £1500 and for some mysterious
reason it has been reduced to instalments.

    The telephone constantly rings from the length and breadth
of the country from people wanting to talk to me about my engines,
chimneys and life style that isn't the same anymore.

    I would have liked to have carried on but theaaggravation
out weighs the money involved.

    Please find first instalments enclosed.

Yours faithfully

It's not right says Fred!

□ HAD it gone wrong, the
BBC would have got it in
the neck for another ill-
conceived stunt .. but
Bolton steeplejack Fred
Dibnah made no mistakes.
In his BBC 2 series of
adventures, A Year With
Fred, on Mondays, he fells
a mill chimney stack so
close to some houses that
£1 million insurance was
taken out.

red Dibnah, TV star

A close call for steeplejack star

Here is the news, we're still waiting for Fred . . .

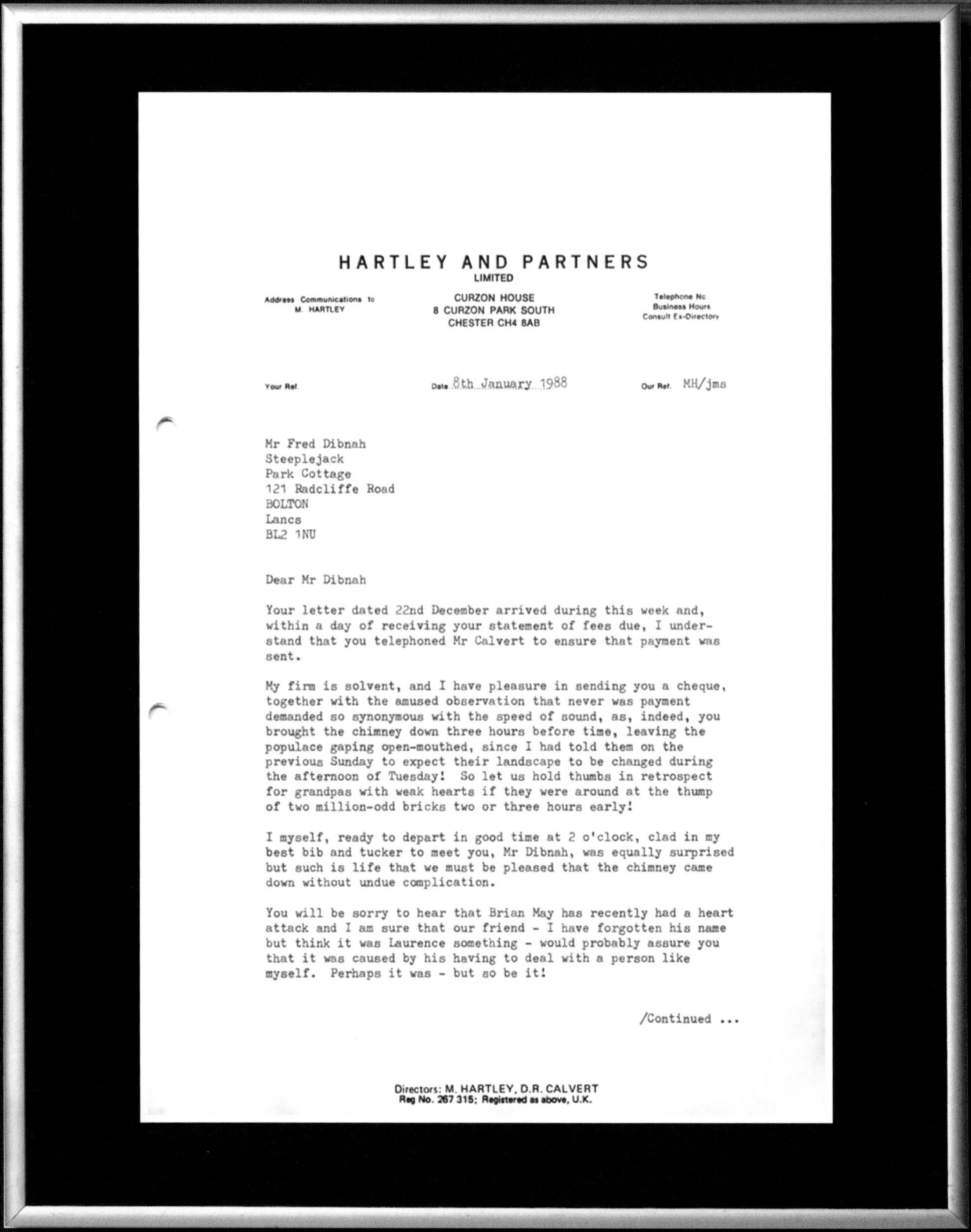

HARTLEY AND PARTNERS
LIMITED

Address Communications to
M. HARTLEY

CURZON HOUSE
8 CURZON PARK SOUTH
CHESTER CH4 8AB

Telephone No.
Business Hours
Consult Ex-Directory

Your Ref.

Date 8th January 1988

Our Ref. MH/jms

Mr Fred Dibnah
Steeplejack
Park Cottage
121 Radcliffe Road
BOLTON
Lancs
BL2 1NU

Dear Mr Dibnah

Your letter dated 22nd December arrived during this week and, within a day of receiving your statement of fees due, I understand that you telephoned Mr Calvert to ensure that payment was sent.

My firm is solvent, and I have pleasure in sending you a cheque, together with the amused observation that never was payment demanded so synonymous with the speed of sound, as, indeed, you brought the chimney down three hours before time, leaving the populace gaping open-mouthed, since I had told them on the previous Sunday to expect their landscape to be changed during the afternoon of Tuesday! So let us hold thumbs in retrospect for grandpas with weak hearts if they were around at the thump of two million-odd bricks two or three hours early!

I myself, ready to depart in good time at 2 o'clock, clad in my best bib and tucker to meet you, Mr Dibnah, was equally surprised but such is life that we must be pleased that the chimney came down without undue complication.

You will be sorry to hear that Brian May has recently had a heart attack and I am sure that our friend - I have forgotten his name but think it was Laurence something - would probably assure you that it was caused by his having to deal with a person like myself. Perhaps it was - but so be it!

/Continued ...

Directors: M. HARTLEY, D.R. CALVERT
Reg No. 267 315; Registered as above, U.K.

Mr Fred Dibnah   8th January 1988

H. & P. Continuation Page   2

I now enclose cheque in the sum of £700, and thank you for your
assistance.

Yours sincerely

M HARTLEY

Enc:

This fantastic and amusing letter from Hartley & Partners was sent
to Fred following the demolition of their factory chimney in 1988.

Fred, the colourful, droll genius

Fred's open to all offers

A CHANCE to meet TV steeplejack Fred Dibnah and demolish a 150ft factory chimney in Cockermouth is being offered to the highest bidder.

Proceeds from the event will go to a local charity and all bids must be submitted by Friday to the Flimby-based construction group, Thomas Armstrong.

The company, who own the 160 year old Derwent Mills chimney, are clearing part of the site to make way for industrial development and housing.

The chimney will be toppled at 3pm on Saturday by setting fire to wooden supports at its base.

Whoever bids the most will light the fire, at the

• **Fred Dibnah**

climax to a fund-raising afternoon organised by Cockermouth Lions.

A special area will be roped off for spectators, with entertainment provided from 1pm. The event is also being filmed by Border Television.

BUILDERS ACCIDENT

Insurers ....

Policy No. 4442

Insured's Name ...... F. DIBNAH

Class of Insurance :—

...... PUBLIC LIABILITY

Annual Premium £ 17 : 10 : -

Renewable at ...... 23rd June 1965

SUBJECT MATTER.

Indemnity ...... £25,000.

....

....

....

....

HINDLEY, KNIGHT & C°. L^{td}

Incorporated Insurance Brokers

89, Newport Street, Bolton.

Kindly examine your Policy and if it is not drawn up in accordance with your intentions please return it to us at once for amendment.

 RADC

121

Chimney climb to danger

POLICE had to coax down a man who diced with death by climbing 250 feet up a mill chimney last night.

The young man, who has not been named, scrambled in his stocking feet up ladders which had been fixed to Darwen's 320 feet high India Mill chimney by Bolton steeplejack Fred Dibnah.

The distressed man, who is thought to have had a domestic dispute, was persuaded by police to inch his way down the icy rungs as horrified onlookers watched.

He is being treated in hospital.

Fred had strung his chain of ladders to the top of the town's famous landmark for a charity stunt last weekend. But it had to be called off because of high winds.

BUT WHAT

-FE RD.

Fred's next challenge

NEWS IN BRIEF

Unkind cut

A TV advert for Vodaphone had Cambridge museum bosses worried.

The advert, featuring steeplejack Fred Dibnah, seemed to show the 170ft chimney of the Museum of Technology in Cheddar's Lane being demolished.

But footage of Mr Dibnah repairing the giant brick chimney was cut together with film of another being blown up.

Just Fred, Not Anybody Special

Nearly 17 years after the BBC first introduced plain-talking Fred Dibnah into our living rooms, life is still on the up for the fearless steeplejack

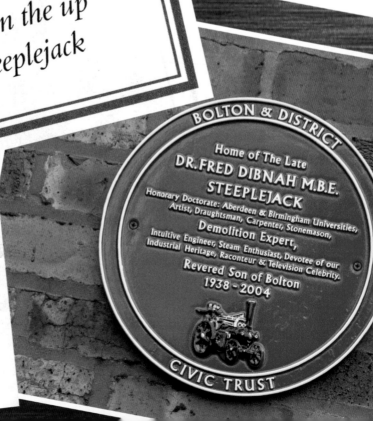

Caleb's Tower

Fred Dibnah gave them free advice
Because it was so tall;
But they ignored those kindly words,
They thought they knew it all.
Fred shook his head and mopped his
        brow
And said "They're bloody barmy!"
So when they pulled those chocks
        away
It flattened Sally Army!   Billy P.

BOLTON & DISTRICT

Home of The Late
DR. FRED DIBNAH M.B.E.
STEEPLEJACK
Honorary Doctorate: Aberdeen & Birmingham Universities,
Artist, Draughtsman, Carpenter, Stonemason,
Demolition Expert,
Intuitive Engineer, Steam Enthusiast, Devotee of our
Industrial Heritage, Raconteur & Television Celebrity.
Revered Son of Bolton
1938 - 2004

CIVIC TRUST

"RIGHT" SAID FRED

JER LIKE THAT

CENTRAL CHANCERY OF THE ORDERS
ST. JAMES'S PALACE
LONDON SW1
OF KNIGHTHOOD

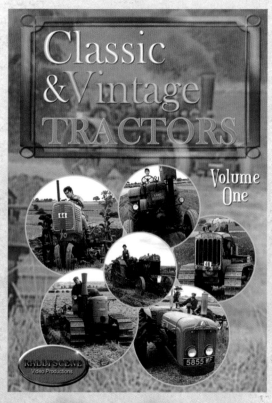

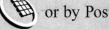

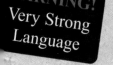

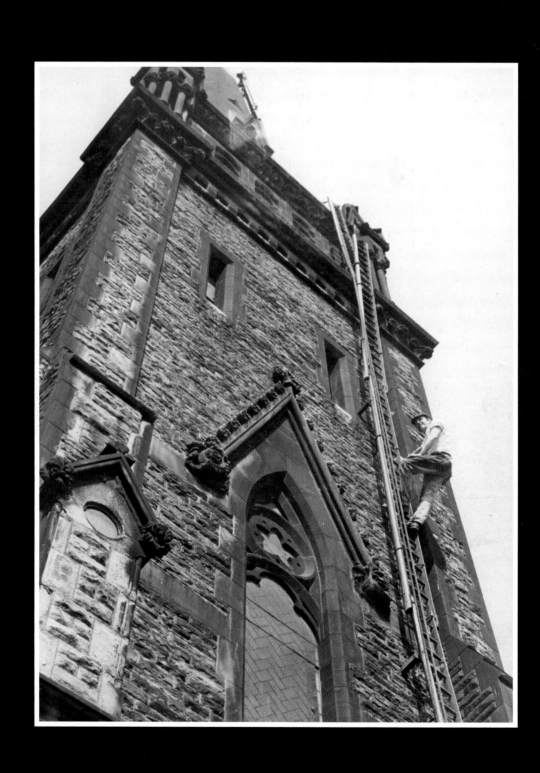

Cloth cap image is OK

Fred's mystery caps the lot!

DEATH-defying steeplejack Fred Dibnah almost fainted after he got a mystery brain infection — from his flat cap!

The chimney demolition king was queueing in the building society to pay a whopping income tax bill when he almost collapsed.

"I thought he was having me on because he was having to pay up," said wife Sue.

She revealed how Fred took to his bed back at their Bolton home and came out in red blotches and hot flushes.

After a series of tests, doctors discovered his brain was being attacked by a germ picked up after he accidentally dropped his cap in some stagnant water.

Fred, 55, who starts a new four-part BBC2 series, Life With Fred, tomorrow week, tells me: A germ got in through a scratch on my scalp.

"It was an alarming experience and could have been very serious. But I'll never get rid of my cap. It makes me look a few years younger by covering my bald head."

If the cap fits, Fred . . .

Fred Dibnah & Sons
Steeplejacks

PARK COTTAGE,
121 RADCLIFFE ROAD, BOLTON BL2 1NU, LANCS.
TEL & FAX: 0204 31303

With Compliments

Telephone:
BOLTON 31303

REPAIRER OF
CHIMNEYS, CHURCH SPIRES, LIGHTNING CONDUCTORS
ERECTED FLAG POLES PAINTED AND REPAIRED : CHIMNEYS FELLED OR
DEMOLISHED : CHIMNEYS BANDED AND REPAIRED : IRON CHIMNEYS PAINTED
AND REPAIRED : WEATHER VANES MADE AND FITTED

Established
1958

F. DIBNAH
STEEPLEJACK
PARK COTTAGE, RADCLIFFE ROAD
BOLTON BL2 1NU
FULLY INSURED

Ocean Mills, Edbro

...............................19....

£   p.

If the company insists on the full amount I request
that the bill of £185 76p be put in hourly rates
with more detail and that Mr. Robinson witnesses the
hydraulic test and if successful issues a certificate
test for 12 months then I will pay the full amount.

P.S. I am not a very Yours faithfully rich man, not a big
company with untold resources

Fully insured repairers of Chimneys and
Spires; Lightning Conductors erected; Flag Poles
...l and repaired; Chimneys felled or demolished;
...ys banded and pointed; Iron Chimneys painted
...a repaired; Weather Vanes made and fitted. Industrial
Archaeological Restoration projects undertaken

Explosion (1938)

THE chief engineer and his assistant at the Honeywell Mill, Hathershaw, had narrow escapes when an explosion occurred in the engine house.

The two men were engaged in their duties when the high pressure valve box blew off with a terrific report which was heard in houses a hundred yards away.

The engine house was filled with escaping steam, and the valve box, which was of solid metal, three feet by two feet, and three inches thick, struck the wall near where the men were standing, and broke into pieces which narrowly missed them, falling at their feet.

Some of the windows were smashed by the concussion, but one of the men had the presence of mind to crawl along the floor through the escaping steam to switch off the engine.

As a result of the smash the mill will be stopped for about two weeks for repairs, and over two hundred operatives will be out of employment.

A Chronicle representative who visited the mill today found several assistants busily engaged in repairing the damage.

Fred Dibnah

Fred Dibnah's famous steam roller covered in snow.